Neo-Classicism in America

Inspiration and Innovation

1810–1840

Introduction by Stuart P. Feld
Essay by Wendell Garrett

April 27 through June 7, 1991

Hirschl & Adler Galleries, Inc.
21 East 70th Street, New York, New York 10021
212 535 8810

EXHIBITION ORGANIZED BY:
Stuart P. Feld

CATALOGUE COORDINATED BY:
Susan E. Menconi
Meredith E. Ward

CATALOGUE ENTRIES WRITTEN BY:
Stuart P. Feld
Joseph Goddu
Bruce Lazarus
Susan E. Menconi
Meredith E. Ward

COVER:
Thomas Doughty
View of the Fairmount Waterworks, Philadelphia,
from the Opposite Side of the Schuylkill River (detail)
No. 76

© 1991 Hirschl & Adler Galleries, Inc.
Library of Congress Catalog Number: 91-071596
ISBN: 0-915057-41-7

Contents

Charles-Honoré Lannuier, *Pier Table, with Winged Female Caryatid Supports* (detail), no. 16

Introduction

Stuart P. Feld

When The American Wing at The Metropolitan Museum of Art opened with great fanfare in 1924, it placed on view the most comprehensive collection ever assembled of American decorative arts — or what was then, more than sixty-five years ago, perceived as "important" in the field. The collection contained many works in various media that are still acknowledged as definitive masterpieces in their respective areas, but it stopped short with a group of so-called Duncan Phyfe furniture and a single table attributed to the very skillful French-emigré cabinetmaker, Charles-Honoré Lannuier, of New York. With these exceptions, the whole aspect of post-Sheraton and -Hepplewhite Neo-Classicism was ignored. Not surprisingly, the later revival and eclectic styles that punctuated the nineteenth century were not represented; it was not until the 1960s that the collection of American decorative arts began to expand systematically beyond a token representation of "Belter" furniture and the glass of the Tiffany Studios.

Fashions exist in the world of collecting and scholarship just as they do in the clothing that we wear and the settings in which we live. At the end of the nineteenth century there had been a flurry of interest in the more ponderous forms of American furniture of the Classical Revival period, even to a point where reproductions were made in great quantity, but the fact that they were marketed as "Colonial" furniture suggests that there was little connoisseurship to differentiate them from the reproductions of eighteenth-century Chippendale furniture that had begun to proliferate during the period around the Centennial of the United States in 1876. The shingle-style cottages designed by the architect H. H. Richardson and his many followers were furnished with a conglomeration of contemporary designs and both period and reproduction Chippendale and other "Colonial" forms that gave the same impure impression of "early American" as did the so-called Queen Anne rooms in which they were placed.

By the 1920s and 1930s the early and "tasteful" furniture designs of Duncan Phyfe and his contemporaries — largely passing under an attribution to Phyfe himself — had gained significant recognition and popularity among a growing band of collectors, and Phyfe chairs and tables and other pieces began to command prices that rivaled those of important Chippendale and Queen Anne examples. The Depression that dampened our spirits and reduced our pocketbooks in the 1930s, and World War II that preoccupied us in the first half of the 1940s decreased interest in art and antique collecting, but as enthusiasm reappeared in the post-War years, it focused heavily on eighteenth-century furniture and, not surprisingly, on the architecture of the Colonial and early Federal periods.

Although, as Lewis Mumford wrote in his prophetic *The Brown Decades* (1931), there was little interest in preserving the diverse and inventive architectural monuments of the nineteenth century, to say nothing of the furnishings that had once ornamented them — by the time we are ready to reappraise them, he lamented, they will have disappeared — nineteenth-century American paintings did begin to gain favor. A growing enthusiasm for American art developed not only among such visionary collectors as Maxim Karolik, who systematically combed the country in search of multiple examples of the work of Martin Johnson Heade, Fitz Hugh Lane, and others to augment the collection of American paintings, mostly early portraits, at the Museum of Fine Arts in Boston, but also among a more modest circle of private collectors, largely based in New York, who helped to rediscover the landscape, still-life, and genre paintings that had emerged during the 1820s and suddenly broadened the taste for American art beyond the traditional subject of portrait painting.

The decorative arts of the Classical Revival remained largely ignored in the post-War years, or at least until interest in them was revived by Jacqueline Kennedy in the early 1960s in her effort to restore The White House to the grandeur and integrity of its early nineteenth-century period and by the late Berry Tracy, Curator of Decorative Arts at The Newark Museum, who in 1963 produced the decorative arts portion of the landmark exhibition, *Classical America 1815–1845*. With the collaboration of Newark's Curator of Painting and Sculpture, Dr. William H. Gerdts, Tracy was able to mount a comprehensive exhibition of the arts of the United States during this important period in American history, and to document this material in an accompanying catalogue that has for years served as a standard reference work in the field.

Indeed, together with the decorative arts volume of the pair of catalogues that accompanied the ground-breaking exhibition, *19th-Century America*, at The Metropolitan Museum of Art in 1970, *Classical America* remains the best general text on the subject of Neo-Classical decorative arts in the United States. Beyond this, bits and pieces in Charles F. Montgomery's *American Furniture — The Federal Period, in the Henry Francis du Pont Winterthur Museum* (1966), various articles such as Jeanne Vibert Sloane's "A Duncan Phyfe bill and the furniture it documents" and others that have occasionally appeared in *The Magazine Antiques,* and brief glimpses here and there in general books or specialized catalogues, such as Gregory R. Weidman's *Furniture in Maryland 1740–1940* (1984) and J. Michael Flanigan's *American Furniture from the Kaufman Collection* (1986), have added current research to a remarkable scarcity of information in the field. It is noteworthy that the last book to appear on Duncan Phyfe was Nancy McClelland's *Duncan Phyfe and the English Regency 1795–1830* (1939), which, together with Charles Over Cornelius's *Furniture Masterpieces of Duncan Phyfe* (1922) and a few magazine articles and museum catalogues, constitutes the essential bibliography on this American artisan of legendary reputation. Lannuier has fared even less well, with only Lorraine Waxman Pearce's unpublished and now out-of-date treatise, *French Influence on American Decorative Arts of the Early Nineteenth Century — The Work of Charles-Honoré Lannuier* (1958), and a number of articles that have appeared over the years, again largely in *Antiques,* to provide information about this important and very talented artisan who left behind a considerable oeuvre of labelled, stamped, and documented furniture. Robert Smith's series of articles on the Philadelphia cabinetmaker Anthony G. Quervelle that appeared in *Antiques* in 1973–74 was really, in retrospect, rather an article on one aspect of a Philadelphia style of this period than a monographic study of the work of one individual. And Page Talbott's pair of articles on Boston classical furniture, published in *Antiques* in 1975 and 1976, was but a tease to a subject of tantalizing delights that will soon be expanded in her forthcoming article on Boston seating furniture of this period in *Antiques* for May 1991. Whereas William V. Elder's catalogue to accompany the exhibition *Baltimore Painted Furniture 1800–1840* at the Baltimore Museum of Art in 1972 nearly exhausts this important subject, the other aspects of Baltimore furniture of the period have remained obscure and inaccessible. That void will soon be filled by Gregory Weidman's forthcoming exhibition, *Classical Maryland 1815–1845,* to be shown at the Maryland Historical Society, Baltimore, in 1993, at the same time as Wendy Cooper's much anticipated *Classical Taste in America 1800–1840* at the Baltimore Museum of Art, which will survey a broad range of the decorative arts — from Maine to New Orleans, and beyond — in this period.

A vast array of French and English books of the late eighteenth and early nineteenth centuries served as the source of inspiration for American furniture and other decorative arts of the Neo-Classical period. Although Percier and Fontaine's *Recueil de Décorations Intérieures,* published in Paris in 1801, provided the stylistic basis for the aesthetic of the French Empire, it was rather the pages of Pierre de la Mésangère's *Collection des Meubles et Objets de Goût,* which appeared as a periodical from 1802 to 1835, that displayed an array of illustrations that could be used by American, as well as English and Continental, craftsmen as a basis for their own designs. (The relationship between Mésangère's designs and American furniture is explored in Joan Woodside's unpublished doctoral dissertation, "French Influence on American Furniture as seen through the Engraved Designs of Pierre de la Mésangère's 'Collections des Meubles et Objets de Goût' Published from 1802 to 1935" [University of Chicago, 1986].) From England came the pattern books issued by Thomas Sheraton, the 1808 *Supplement to the London Chair-Makers' and Carvers' Book of Prices for Workmanship,* and other publications that offered lingering references to an older, yet still relevant style, while Thomas Hope's *Household Furniture and Interior Decoration* (1801), and his *Designs for Household Furniture,* published posthumously in 1812, gave a quick introduction to the more modern, archaeological styles quickly gaining popularity. And Rudolph Ackermann's *The Repository of Arts, Literature, Commerce, . . .,* which appeared monthly from 1809 to 1828, and George Smith's *Household Furniture* (1808) and his *The Cabinet-Maker's and Upholsterer's Guide* (1826) offered variations and permutations of every conceivable classical motif and composition, both for craftsmen at home and for those across the sea who were attempting to provide their own clientele with what was most fashionable and up-to-date.

The products that resulted from the cabinetmaking shops in Boston, New York, Philadelphia, and other places were finally much more indigenously American than specific imitations of an illustration or illustrations in a single book. Except perhaps for an occasional piece produced by Lannuier that was a slavish imitation of a specific French Empire design, most American furniture of this period was an amalgam of sources that were combined and recombined to produce works that characteristically are quickly identifiable as American rather than English or French. And if the style of furniture made in Boston by Isaac Vose and Sons, Emmons and Archibald, William Fisk, or one of their contemporaries seems both stylistically consistent and yet different from what was going on elsewhere, it helps to define a local, or Boston, style that may have originally developed from the dominance, not now identified, of a single cabinetmaker who actually became the progenitor of an entire style. The same may be said of Philadelphia, where the names of Ephraim Haines and Henry Connelly, and Quervelle, in different generations, have mistakenly tended to define the oeuvre of individuals rather than the character of a "school." In New York the exposure accorded to Duncan Phyfe has given his name to a whole style and period, even though examples labelled or documented by Lannuier (see no. 4), Michael Allison (see no. 5), and others now confirm the existence of a local style, rather than the prodigious output of a single individual or shop. What the genesis of that style was remains an important question that would appear not to be beyond the capacity of modern art historical scholarship.

Similarly, it seems strange that we know so little about so many other aspects of the decorative arts of the United States of this period and beyond. Although most American painters and sculptors of the nineteenth century have been the subject of exhaustive monographic or group studies, much in the field of silver, ceramics, glass, and lighting remains to be investigated. Why, for example, should we know so much about early Venetian, or German, or Dutch glass, and yet not be able to isolate the production of various glass houses in New England in the 1820s and 1830s? As for silver, from surviving examples we can deduce that relatively little was produced in Boston, that New York silver was often commonplace, and that a half dozen or so artisans in Philadelphia made silver of spectacular quality and design. What was the relationship among these Philadelphia silversmiths? Although the "taste" of the silver made by the firm of Fletcher & Gardiner and by Thomas Fletcher alone is distinctive and quickly identifiable, certain die-rolled borders and cast elements used by them also appear on the work of other Philadelphia silversmiths. Were these elements, clearly not imported since they do not appear in English and French production of the period, made by a single local specialist, or were they made by several silversmiths who both used them in their own work and also made them available to their competitors? Only a focused study, based on the increasing number of examples known to us, may provide the answers.

Years ago an attempt was made to use ormolu mounts on American Neo-Classical furniture as a basis for attribution. The validity of this could quickly be challenged — identical mounts, for example, appear on a Boston pier table (see no. 51) and a New York secretary (see no. 14) in this exhibition — but little information about the mounts themselves has been learned. Although individual pieces of American furniture of this period often sport English, French, and occasionally American-made sand-cast mounts, their more immediate source for cabinetmakers here has not been clearly established. Presumably, retailers like Baldwin Gardiner and J. and I. Cox in New York had a supply of such material, but certain cabinetmakers may have had direct contacts abroad. One underlying American denominator seems to have been a make-do attitude with respect to the use of ormolu mounts, gilt beading, brass rosettes, and so forth, certainly related to an occasional lack of supply or lack of variety. Whether the design for a piece of furniture came first and the metalwork that was to adorn it was then selected from what was available locally, or whether the availability of specific ormolu or gilt elements inspired the design of a piece of furniture remains uncertain and but one of many questions, small and large, that are yet to be answered.

❧❧❧

This exhibition features a group of objects from Boston, New York, Philadelphia, Baltimore, and Washington, as well as works produced in England, France, and Italy for the American market, which have been somewhat organized by location, and within that structure somewhat loosely by date. Some of the objects are well-known through previous publications and exhibitions, while others have recently come to light, or have at least not previously been shown or published. The general coordination of the catalogue has fallen to Susan E. Menconi and Meredith E. Ward; individual entries have been written by them, as well as by Joseph Goddu, Bruce Lazarus, and myself, oftentimes with research very capably done by Sandra K. Feldman and Arleen Pancza-Graham. Ellwood C. Parry and Howard Merritt, both veteran Cole scholars, Julia C. Oehmig and Erik Jorgenson of the Pejepscot Historical Society, Brunswick, Maine, Bill Barry of the Portland Public Library, Portland, Maine, Diana Arecco of the New-York Historical Society, and Donald L. Fennimore, Jr., of Winterthur have all made valuable contributions to this exhibition and publication. The entire manuscript has been organized, typed, and brought to readiness for publication by Marissa G. Boyescu, who has also done some research, and has handled many of the details of the loans in concert with our registrars Mary Sheridan and Richard Sica. A very special thanks goes to Wendell Garrett for his erudite and provocative essay which gives a taste of the social and political background of the Classical Revival in the United States.

Our gratitude must also go to Gloria and Richard Manney for the loan of their glorious New York cellarette, to various other private lenders who have desired to remain anonymous, and to Sherry Fowble and Eleanor McD. Thompson at The Henry Francis du Pont Winterthur Museum, Peter Kenny and Suzanne Boorsch at The Metropolitan Museum of Art, and Barry Harwood at The Brooklyn Museum, who have helped to secure loans from their institutions. Our thanks also go to Deanne Levison, and Albert, Harold, and Robert Sack of the firm of Israel Sack, to Alexander Acevedo of Alexander Galleries, to Anthony Stuempfig, and to Richard York for their generous contributions to the exhibition. Cumulatively, all of these people and all of the beautiful works in this exhibition add up to a salute to The Campaign for Winterthur, which the opening of this exhibition honors and benefits.

Novus Ordo Seclorum: A New Order of the Ages

Wendell Garrett

Crafting a nation was heady business, and the framers of the Constitution approached it as men of destiny. Likening themselves to the fabled "lawgivers" of ancient times, the leading delegates at Philadelphia shared James Madison's solemn conviction that they would "decide forever the fate of republican government." They brought a vast knowledge of history and a long tradition of civic humanism with them to the Convention in May of 1787. They departed four months later having fashioned a frame of government that not only necessitated a redefinition of the terms in which the theory and ideology of civic humanism had been discussed, but also introduced a new concept to the discourse — that of Federalism — and in the doing, created *novus ordo seclorum.* They devised a new order out of materials prescribed by the ages. They dared to believe that the United States could show the world what good government was. They were obsessed with the mission of America as asylum, America as redeemer, America as exporter of the spirit of liberty, America as the "seat of another golden age." They dreamed of achieving that rarefied state of stability and order through a national government — a government elected by, representative of, and responsible to, the people: in short, a republic based on the model of the Greek city-states and especially Imperial Rome. These Olympians rose above petty self-interest and local prejudice to produce what Prime Minister William Gladstone would call, on the occasion of the Constitution's centennial, "the most remarkable work known to me in modern times to have been produced by the human intellect, at a single stroke (so to speak), in its application to political affairs." Alfred North Whitehead later said that the two occasions in history "when people in power did what needed to be done about as well as you can imagine its being possible", were the age of Augustus and during the framing of the American Constitution.

Classical antiquity haunted the Federal imagination. "The Roman Republic," Alexander Hamilton wrote in *The Federalist,* No. 34, "attained to the utmost height of human greatness." The founding Fathers — classicists who read Polybius, Plutarch, Cicero, Sallust, and Tacitus — embarked on a perilous adventure of establishing a republic, and for landmarks they peered across the gulf of centuries to Greece and Rome, which they saw as the noblest achievements of free men aspiring to govern themselves. The American Revolution itself had been partly guided by classical ideals. The Latin rendition of the motto from Virgil's *Aeneid* on the Great Seal of the United States of 1782, *annuit coeptis* — God has favored our undertaking — contains thirteen letters, as does *e pluribus unum* — one out of many. The institutions as well as the symbols of this first generation of the American Republic were markedly Greco-Roman in inspiration. In this conviction the senior legislative body in the United States was called the Senate — the name of the elders' council of the Roman Republic — and met in the Capitol — a building named after one of the seven hills of Rome — which was itself built on a famous Greco-Roman model. These leaders liked to "look back with reverence" to classical antiquity as they sculpted their heroes in togas, named new communities Athens and Sparta, Ithaca and Troy, organized the Society of the Cincinnati, assigned shelves of Latin texts to the young, and built Greek temples for their banks, schools, and homes.

Classical thought clearly shaped the values of educated Americans in the early Republic. Greek and Roman political theory and history — what Joseph Story called "the prescriptive wisdom of antiquity" — contained lessons for American citizens to master and apply. Hamilton copied long sections from Plutarch and called himself "Paulus" to Thomas Jefferson's "Scipio" and John Adams' "Brutus" in justifying his own classicism in 1789. Adams announced: "I should as soon think of closing all my window shutters, to enable me to see, as of banishing the Classicks." For him, "the Roman constitution formed the noblest people and the greatest power that has ever existed." Jefferson expressed the prevailing viewpoint of his generation in 1814 when he said: "For classical learning I have ever been a zealous advocate." But there was also a warning: for the grandeur that was Rome had come to an inglorious end. From the calm skepticism of Edward W. Montagu's *Reflections on the Rise and Fall of Ancient Republicks* (1760) to the aggressive skepticism of Edward Gibbon's *Decline and Fall* (1776), the analogy of past and present acquired a new apocalyptic force: could the United States of America with the new wealth and crass materialism, the decay of morality and religion, the puzzling mixture of decadence and majesty, hope to escape the classical fate? Invoking classical republican models, aware of the classical cyclical theory of political change and the impermanence of political systems, the Founding Fathers had frequent recourse to the "pure fountains" of antiquity and seized upon the doctrine of mixed government and separation of powers in the republican government found in ancient states for a remedy. And Latin and Greek were essential to this purpose.

Washington, the Federal city, was a monument to great expectations. The French-born engineer Pierre Charles L'Enfant's design for a capital was imaginative and ambitious. Each branch of government was to be physically separate; connecting the branches were broad avenues that cut diagonally across the gridiron arrangement of numbered and lettered streets. L'Enfant urged that the public buildings be built in brick and stone in the style of Greek and Roman temples. But reality did not conform to desire. It was "the City of Magnificent Intentions," wrote Charles Dickens in 1842; "such as it is it is likely to remain." Construction of the public buildings was painfully slow: eight years passed before the President's House was habitable, seven before Congress could deliberate in the Capitol. And yet the dream of a planned monument to classical republicanism persisted.

In its intent, its classical design, and its unfinished chaos, Washington symbolized the new nation. Just as L'Enfant wished to bring classical grandeur to formless woods on the banks of the Potomac, those who framed the Constitution hoped to impose a model Republic on a raw wilderness. On paper, the design was a perfect construct of Enlightenment rationality and good sense; in reality, the Republic existed as an almost ungovernable collection of diverse elements caught up in an atmosphere of rapid and unpredictable change. Many observers feared that a national government based on republican principles would prove impossible when stretched to the unheard-of scale of the American continent. "You might as well attempt to rule Hell by Prayer," wrote a typical anti-Federalist in 1787.

These anxieties were based upon hard realities; John Adams spoke for his generation in 1812 when he described the union as "a brittle China vase" and "a Palace of Glass" easily destroyed. Sectional differences among Americans in the new nation remained as apparent as the common qualities that had united them earlier against England. Differences of ethnic origin, culture, occupation, and class fragmented the Republic into regional groupings of pluralistic and diversified states. These centrifugal forces, given the added innovations constantly being introduced by science and technology, appeared to defy all attempts at harnessing them. This threatening sense of self-destruction, this pervasive self-doubt, this intense conviction of the improbability of their undertaking were all nourished by the unfortunate speculations of some of the French philosophes about the lessened potency of nature in the New World. Jefferson's *Notes on the State of Virginia* — with all of its meteorological charts of rainfall and wind velocity, its elaborate comparisons of European and American animal life — was obsessed with the sense of the uniqueness of America. America was different, he argued, and was immune from the forces of history and the laws of history. Thus, while Americans of Jefferson's generation longed for stability and predictability, they lived in a world of chaotic change that was at odds with their ideal. The result was a society of contrasts and a people of paradox — crude and civilized, violent and peaceful, exuberant and restrained. One spread-eagle Fourth of July orator in Philadelphia in 1817 pictured the American success and exceptionalism as a golden column of classical architecture. All that America had accomplished, he explained, had been achieved against the experience of history. The result was that "we stand alone . . . . We have been spared by the hand of time, which sweeps in its course nations and countries — we have been left like a golden column, standing firmly erect, and surrounded by the crumbling fragments of other republics."

The forces of change were many. European visitors during the first half of the nineteenth century were astounded not only by the size of the new Republic, but were also struck by its emptiness. Between 1800 and 1850 the population of slightly more than five million persons quintupled by immigration and natural fertility. And this dramatic growth increased mobility as the center of population steadily moved west. "In most places there is not a single grown man or woman native to the place, or indeed, to the territory," commented one traveler in 1847; "many of them have moved a number of times, always farther west, and they will very likely do so again." The driving force behind this restiveness was cheap or free land. We were a nation of farmers and more than four-fifths of the population in 1800 earned their living from the soil. The land was so rich and plentiful that surpluses were generally available for the market. In every region, the growth of commercial agriculture created a phenomenon unknown in the Old World: land, like the cottage industries of the hearth and home, became a commodity to be bought and sold.

Commerce encouraged urbanization and manufacturing, and cities along the seaboard grew with the market. The small farmers of the hinterland served the needs of maritime entrepreneurs, and the profits earned financed new ventures, built factories and homes, paid wages, and filtered down to support churches, hospitals, schools, and colleges. The census of 1790 found only six cities with more than 8,000 inhabitants. In that year Philadelphia was the most important urban center with a population of 42,520, but it was soon to lose its preeminence in trade and population to New York. The New York population of 33,131 nearly tripled by 1810 and surpassed Philadelphia. The lead which New York acquired by 1810 would be insured by the opening of the Erie Canal in 1825 that brought bulky freight from the Great Lakes region to the port. The city with the oldest traditions in the United States was Boston, but Boston allowed New York and Philadelphia to outstrip it in shipping and business enterprise. While Boston was the third city in population in 1790, with a population of 18,038, it had fallen to fourth place by 1820, behind Baltimore, the fastest growing city in America, which prospered from the tobacco trade of Virginia and Maryland and the grain trade out of Pennsylvania. And by 1800 the coastal cities and surrounding countryside were beginning to experience the first effects of the Industrial Revolution — changes that Americans greeted with breathless optimism. The most visible signs of change were in New England, where individual entrepreneurs combined native inventiveness with strikingly modern techniques of production and organization to create the forerunners of the factory system. The high-output, low-unit cost production initiated by the textile industry in the region spread to other, more sophisticated enterprises, such as clockmaking and the manufacture of firearms with mass production assembled from precisely tooled interchangeable parts. The Revolution was also at work in the central Atlantic states, where foundries and forges smelted and converted iron for the production of nails, horseshoes, guns, tools, and the manufacture of increasingly sophisticated steam engines.

The spirit of enterprise fed on many sources. Territorial expansion opened up a continent of almost limitless assets, promising the industrious artisans and craftsmen success and achievement. The egalitarian ideology of the Revolutionary War encouraged mobility and raised expectations. The Industrial Revolution introduced the tools of technology to economic enterprise. Running through all these forces of change was the American capacity for innovation. It was not so much innovation in the sense of discovery as innovation in the sense that Americans could adapt their resources to solve problems. "Our greatest thinkers," one practical man boasted, "are not in the library, nor the capitol, but in the machine shop." Thus, the steam engine was invented in England, but the steamboat was invented and perfected in the United States. In a justly celebrated passage to his wife in 1780, John Adams proclaimed with all deliberateness: "It is not indeed the fine Arts, which our Country requires. The Usefull, the mechanic Arts, are those which We have occasion for in a young Country." Even among the staunchest advocates of classical learning in America, the premise of utilitarianism was that the imperatives of building a new country required more practical knowledge than a single-minded study of the classics. William Livingston of New York argued: "We want hands . . . more than heads. The most intimate acquaintance with the classics, will not remove our oaks; nor a taste for the *Georgics* cultivate our lands. Many of our young people are knocking their heads against the

Iliad, who should employ their hands in clearing our swamps and draining our marshes. Others are musing, in cogitation profound, on the arrangement of a syllogism, while they ought to be guiding the tail of a plow."

Utility and austerity were at the confluence of classical republican theories, which helps to explain the intellectual reaction against the frivolity and flippancy, deception and irrationality, of the Rococo. This was no modish change from one fashion to another; neoclassicism was as radical a rejection of and revulsion from the *genre pittoresque* to the *goût grec* as the fiery, rebellious democratic revolutions in America and France against the *ancien régime.*

The study and use of classical antiquities was thus regarded as a means of penetrating the eternally valid truths which were thought to underlie the superficial diversities of the visible world. Winckelmann revealed a deeper purpose when he declared: "There is only one way for the moderns to become great and perhaps unequalled: by imitating the Ancients." To him, the "noble simplicity and calm grandeur" of antique statues were in themselves ennobling. The term "neoclassical," or the more obviously opprobrious adjective "pseudo-classical," were pejorative at the time; it is important to remember that what we now call "neoclassicism" was described by artists and critics at the time as, quite simply, the "true" or "correct" style, an art of universal significance and eternal validity. In place of the rococo Olympus of amorous gods and licentious goddesses and that perennial *fête champêtre* in which the *jeunesse dorée* philandered through an eternal, langourous afternoon amidst *rocaille* ornament — what Baudelaire in 1855 called "an excess of gay and charming frivolities" — one now finds themes and subjects of a very different kind: a new style that was strongly didactic in intention, offering sobering lessons in the more homely virtues, and stoic exemplars of unspoilt and uncorrupted simplicity, of abstinence and self-restraint, of noble self-sacrifice and heroic patriotism.

In this political discourse the word "virtue" took on many shades of meaning, drawing upon secular theory and Protestant ideas about righteousness. J.G.A. Pocock has dealt brilliantly with "The Americanization of Virtue" in his *Machiavellian Moment,* showing how the classical republican definition of virtue overlapped with Anglo-American Protestant values: the personal virtues of industry and frugality deemed essential to a good citizen were virtually the same as those prescribed by Protestant morality. The persistent anxiety about the conspicuous consumption of foreign luxury goods seemed a sign of flagging public spirit and Christian faith. The anti-Rococo criticism was frequently directed against the rich and the corrupting or trivializing influence of their taste for luxury. In 1790 Gouverneur Morris wrote George Washington some rather gratuitous but revealing advice about furnishing the new presidential mansion: "I think it of very great importance to fix the taste of our country properly, and I think your example will go very far in that respect. It is therefore my wish that everything about you should be substantially *good and majestically plain,* made to endure." The aesthetic qualities which artists and craftsmen wished to embody in their works, and which theorists extolled, had ethical connotations — truth, purity, nobility, honesty, "majestic plainness" or ostentatious austerity.

Antiquity was to be imitated, not copied. To quote Winckelmann again, "the opposite of independent thought is for me the copy not the imitation." This is an important distinction, for the practice of copying either antiquity or common nature, except as a part of the process of learning, was generally agreed to be reprehensible. The New England-born Horatio Greenough, who went to Italy in 1825 to practice sculpture, said, "I contend for Greek principles, not Greek things." Only in one respect was the precise copying of antiquities advocated. Artists representing subjects from ancient history were required to render faithfully the details of costume and decoration, not for any merely pedantic reason, but in order to reinforce moral truth with archaeological accuracy. "My principles of good taste are rigid in Grecian architecture," Benjamin Henry Latrobe wrote to Jefferson in 1807, but added: "Our religion requires a church wholly different from the temples, our legislative assemblies and our courts of justice, buildings of entirely different principles from their basilicas; and our amusements could not possibly be performed in their theatres & amphitheatres."

The vogue for making the Grand Tour remained almost a ceremonial *rite de passage* for English and American gentlemen well into the nineteenth century. "The grand object of travelling," pronounced Doctor Samuel Johnson in the eighteenth century, "is to see the shores of the Mediterranean. On these shores were the four great Empires of the world; the Assyrian, the Persian, the Grecian, and the Roman. All our religion, almost all our law, almost all our arts, almost all that sets us above savages, has come to us from the shores of the Mediterranean." Perhaps the most specific embodiment of the taste for classical antiquity was the existence of the Society of Dilettanti in England. Qualification for membership depended on having made the Grand Tour: Horace Walpole rather sourly interpreted this as "the nominal qualification for membership is having been in Italy, and the real one being drunk." By its mere existence the Society indirectly influenced public taste toward classicism by publishing large tomes on the architecture and archaeology of the classical world. Even if they were not able to go on the Grand Tour, there was no lack of opportunity for budding connoisseurs to exercise their taste.

While it is true that the second half of the eighteenth century was the Golden Age of classical learning in America, few Americans braved the rigors of an ocean crossing to travel extensively in Europe. During his stay in France in the 1780s Jefferson toured southern France (where he fell in love with the Maison Carré at Nîmes) and northern Italy, what he called his "peep into Elysium." In 1805 Washington Irving climbed Vesuvius, stopped at Herculaneum, and described the sights in Pompeii; in his journal he expressed chagrin that the King of the Two Sicilies, living in luxury in Naples, had not provided funds to continue the excavations of Pompeii. The Philadelphian Nicholas Biddle visited Greece in 1806 and wrote: "the soil of Greece is sacred to genius and to letters. . . . The two great truths in the world are the Bible and Grecian architecture." With the classical pilgrimage of four young Americans from Harvard College — Edward Everett, George Ticknor, Joseph Green Cogswell, and George Bancroft — who went to Göttingen University between 1815 and 1820 to absorb and bring back

German scholarship to Cambridge, the desolate country around Paestum began to be more frequently visited. When James Fenimore Cooper visited the classical sites in 1828–30, he thought Herculaneum of greater importance than Pompeii; there is, he wrote, "sublimity in the catastrophe of Herculaneum, a grandeur in desolation, that has no parallel." He made the popular ascent of Vesuvius and also ventured to Paestum. Like many others of his era, Cooper dated the ruins of Paestum to the time of the pyramids of Egypt and ventured to place them in the new civilization that emerged after the biblical flood. "What a speck does the history of America become in this long vista of events."

The new nation boasted a galaxy of political and cultural leaders, mostly the product of a classical education, who were quite literally incomparable. They adopted the classicism of the Federal and Empire styles as their official artistic canon and the cult of antiquity almost as a secular religion. One common denominator of this generation was education: all of them knew Plutarch and Thucydides, Cicero and Tacitus. The stoic virtues of Republican Rome were upheld as standards not merely for the arts but also for political behavior and private morality. They all appear to have absorbed the same maxims of conduct, to have studied the same texts, to have subscribed to the same philosophical concepts, and to have drawn inspiration throughout their lives from the study and reading of the classics. Their reading in and meditation upon the classics were practical and purposeful as repositories of timeless models for guidance in republicanism and civic virtue. And these lofty ideals of the antique affected and influenced the everyday world of the decorative arts with a new aesthetic — cool precision of line, delicacy of detail, attractive contrasts of textures, and opulent simplicity and easy elegance. It was an Enlightenment movement in America based on faith in the perfectibility, the essential goodness and reasonableness of humanity, which found political expression in the American Revolution. It aimed to produce an art of eternal and universal relevance; under its impact, perhaps for the first time in history, nearly all of the artists and craftsmen of the Old World and the New seem to have been striving towards a common end, however different their starting points and however conflicting their views on how they could reach their goal. It was an era of change: where Federal craftsmen had sought inspiration in the purest and most primitive forms of antique Greek art, those of the Empire period turned to the florid opulence of Imperial Rome; the abstemious severity of the Doric was replaced by Corinthian richness and splendor.

The United States in this middle period of its history was, by the Constitution, both a nation and a collection of states and sections. Its furniture and silver and other decorative arts, like its society and culture, displayed regional differences and local diversities that were fundamental — a tangled skein of characteristics varying in form, materials, construction, and decoration, which, in their complexities and ambiguities, somehow are bound up and unified into a style we call uniquely American. Americans in the new nation were conscious not only of being new, but of being different. They gradually began to realize that it was a distinct advantage to the United States, as Jefferson said, to have "the American hemisphere to itself." It might well be, they concluded, that the United States, because it was new and different, was possibly superior to the old nations, and that God had willed it so. "We are destined to be a barrier against the return of ignorance and barbarism," Jefferson wrote to his old friend John Adams; "Old Europe will have to lean on our shoulders, and to hobble along by our side . . . as she can."

The rich diversity of American decorative arts objects and paintings in this exhibition can only be understood in the context of the pluralistic and paradoxical society living under our magisterial Constitution — a society of multiple allegiances and mixed interests that held the individual citizen in a sort of loose social orbit. Unlike any other western nation, we were a people of contrasts: a nation born of revolt that was moderate, yet genuinely revolutionary; a society that was liberal in its ideals, yet conservative in its behavior; united in its divisions, and divided in its unity. *E pluribus unum* was not an idly chosen motto for the society and the culture of the new Republic. This young nation — shaped by memory and reshaped by hope — was both forerunner and archetype, and for that reason, if for no other, it commands the respect of history. These Americans went in search of something to which all but a few men aspire; they found a larger portion of it than all but a few will ever know.

NEW YORK

CHARLES-HONORE LANNUIER
(1779–1819; active in the United States 1803–1819), New York

1.

Neo-Classical Bed, about 1810

Mahogany, secondary woods painted verde antique and gilded, with brass filleted crests and castors, 52½ x 88½ x 55 in. Stamped (twice, on each rail): H. LANNUIER, NEW YORK

The French emigré cabinetmaker Charles-Honoré Lannuier enjoyed a brief but distinguished career in New York. He became a leader in the production of fashionable furniture and through his knowledge of French skills and styles helped to establish the Empire style in New York.

One of the earlier examples of Lannuier's work in New York, this handsome bed reflects a profound knowledge of French styles, particularly that of the Directoire. In the early nineteenth century there was a considerable French population in New York, and French fashions were considered extremely stylish.

This bed is constructed of the finest quality mahogany throughout and finished on all four sides. It is stamped with the name of its maker in a manner consistent with French tradition. Lannuier's stamp, or *estampille,* included his own name, as well as that of his adopted city, New York.

Another bed of similar form, with two eagle terminals and paw feet, but designed to be placed along a wall, is published in Nancy McClelland, *Duncan Phyfe and the English Regency 1795–1830* (1939), p. 192 pl. 175. Two additional beds of essentially similar design have recently appeared, but with substantial alterations.

STEPHEN RICHARD
(active 1802–1839), New York

2.
Tea or Coffee Urn, about 1812

Silver, 14⅝ x 12⅛ in. (through the handles)
Signed and inscribed (with engraved signature, under the base): 112 Oz./S. Richard Fecit/No 160 Broad Way New York Sterling Silver; (with engraved signature, inside the cover): S. Richard fecit
Engraved (above the spout): GSSC [monogram] [and a crest of a boar's head]

Apprenticed to the New York silversmith Hugh Wishart, whose touch occasionally appears on his silver, Stephen Richard was apparently one of the most accomplished silversmiths working in New York during the Neo-Classical period. This elaborate urn suggests that he was thoroughly familiar with English Regency forms and ornamentation. The bright-cut borders are a carry-over from Federal designs and anticipate the appearance of die-rolled bands that were to become the standard form of ornamentation on his (see no. 18) and other Classical Revival silver after about 1815. The four heads of oriental men that support the handles foreshadow the use of cast ornament in Empire designs.

    Richard's unusual engraved signature on the bottom also gives the weight as "112 Oz.," the term "Sterling Silver," which was rarely used during this early period, and his address of 160 Broad Way, where, according to the New York City directories, he worked from 1809 to 1812. The identity of the original owner has not been established, either through the engraved initials or the crest of a boar's head.

Private collection

JOHN RUBENS SMITH
(1775–1849)

3.
Arms of the City of New York, 1815

Watercolor on paper, 16 x 22 in.

EXHIBITED: Museum of the Borough of Brooklyn, New York, 1985, *From Brooklyn to the Sea: Ships, Seafarers and New York Harbor*, no. 2 illus., no. 54 in checklist, lent by M. Knoedler & Co., New York

EX COLL.: Dr. Horton, Long Island, New York; to [John Fleming, Inc., New York, and M. Knoedler & Co., New York, in 1969]; to [M. Knoedler & Co., New York, until 1986]

John Rubens Smith was born in London in 1775, and studied and exhibited there at the Royal Academy. By 1809 Smith had come to America, settling in Boston, where he taught drawing, painting, and the science of perspective. He moved to New York in 1814 and again conducted art classes until 1827.

According to Marian S. Carson, who has made a study of Smith's work, this drawing is the cartoon for the transparent banner that the artist created for the New York celebration of peace in 1815, after the War of 1812. It is a free rendering of the Seal of the City of New York, established in 1686 and revised in 1784. The artist's version includes an American Indian, emblematic of the first inhabitants of Manhattan Island, and a sailor, symbolizing New York as a port city. The coat-of-arms at center shows the windmill and beaver, references to New York as a Dutch settlement, the beaver referring in particular to the city's fur trading business. The two flour barrels symbolize New York as a prime exporter of flour. The eagle, emblem of the United States, replaced the crown of England in 1784, just after the Revolution.

CHARLES-HONORE LANNUIER
(1779–1819; active in the United States 1803–1819), New York

4.
Armchair, 1812

Mahogany, with rosewood and brass inlay, 35¼ in. high

RECORDED: *cf.* Mary Martin Craigmyle, "Chairs by Lannuier at New York's City Hall," in *The Magazine Antiques*, XCVII (Feb. 1970), pp. 258–59 // Mary Beth Betts, *The Governor's Room, City Hall, New York* (1983), p. 8

Once the cornerstone of the new New York City Hall (see no. 24) was laid in 1803, the City began to commission the leading artists and artisans of the day to provide its furnishings. Between 1804 and 1824 the Common Council ordered full-length "official" portraits of New York and national worthies from John Trumbull, John Wesley Jarvis, Samuel Lovett Waldo, Thomas Sully, John Vanderlyn, and Samuel F. B. Morse, among others. On July 13, 1812, the Council approved payment to one "H. Lannuier" for "Mahogany chairs etc.

for Common Council $409.," which was in response to a bill submitted by Charles-Honoré Lannuier on April 15, 1812, for, among other items, "24 mahogany arm chairs [at] $14." This chair is part of that original set, some of which are seen in Charles Burton's drawing of the interior of the Governor's Room at City Hall in 1831 (see illustration). It retains its original curious bulbous terminations of the front legs, derived from a plate in Sheraton, whereas the ones remaining at City Hall, together with those added to the set at a later date, have had the legs cut and castors provided.

The chair is further distinguished by the waterleaf carved supports for the arms, in a style and manner generally credited to Duncan Phyfe, a carved tablet with ribbons and crossed flags, as well as four inlayed brass stars at the ends of the crest rail and above the front legs that are typical of Lannuier's style and are seen in a number of other pieces by him.

Private collection

Charles Burton. *Governor's Room, City Hall, New York City,* 1831. Courtesy of The New-York Historical Society, N.Y.C. (not in exhibition).

MICHAEL ALLISON
(active 1800–1845), New York

5.
Sofa, about 1810–15

Mahogany with brass castors,
36 x 80½ x 31½ in.
Stencilled (on inside of rear seat rail): M.
ALLISON/Cabinet Maker/42 & 44 Vesey
Street/Near Bear Market/NEW YORK

New York cabinetmaker Michael Allison
worked in a variety of styles, from
Hepplewhite to Empire. This sofa bears a
very rare stencil that includes an address

where Allison was in business from 1806
to 1815. It is extremely close in style to
the work of the celebrated cabinetmaker
Duncan Phyfe, and confirms that much
New York furniture of this style and
period that has routinely been ascribed to
Phyfe is actually by others, and that the
so-called Phyfe style is more accurately a
New York style. Lannuier, too (see no. 4),
and scores of other cabinetmakers must
have produced quantities of this tasteful
reeded furniture that ultimately derive
from the plates of Thomas Sheraton's
various design books.

Israel Sack, Inc.

23

Attributed to DUNCAN PHYFE
(1768–1854), New York

6.
Pair of Curule Side Chairs,
about 1810–15

Mahogany, with gilt brass paw feet,
33½ in. high

New York chairs incorporating curule legs,
lyre (see no. 8) and harp backs, and
various carved elements, including sheaves
of wheat, thunder bolts, swags, etc., have
traditionally been associated with the shop
of Duncan Phyfe, but they must rather
represent a local style that was adopted by
a whole group of New York and New
York-area cabinetmakers in the early
nineteenth century.

These side chairs (one illustrated), of
a type and design usually attributed to
Phyfe, ultimately derive their curule legs
from a Roman magistrate's folding chair,
but more immediately take their cue from
a design for a stool with crossed side
supports published in the 1808 *Supplement
to the London Chair-Makers' and Carvers' Book
of Prices for Workmanship*.

Consummate examples of flawless
workmanship and impeccable proportion,
these chairs represent the extraordinary
quality of much of the tasteful, carved and
reeded furniture made in New York in the
second decade of the nineteenth century.
Made both upholstered, as here, or with
caned seats that could be supplied with
squabs or winter seats, they were usually
embellished with beautifully cast and gilt
animal paw feet and brass tacks that
harmonized with the ormolu and gilt brass
hardware on other furniture in a room.

The Henry Francis du Pont Winterthur
Museum

Attributed to DUNCAN PHYFE
(1768–1854), New York

7.
Neo-Classical Lyre-Back Piano Stool,
about 1810–15

Mahogany, partially ebonized, with brass
castors and stringing, 30½ in. high

RECORDED: *American Antiques from the Israel
Sack Collection* (1989), p. 2536 no. P6207

ON DEPOSIT: The Metropolitan Museum
of Art, New York, 1971

This expertly carved and well-proportioned piano stool incorporates many of
the features found on documented
Duncan Phyfe furniture. These details
include finely reeded stiles flanking a lyre-
shaped splat, beautifully scrolled arms, a
crest rail crisply carved with leaves and
acorns, and a turned and reeded urn-
shaped shaft raised on saber legs
terminating in carved animal paw feet.

Israel Sack, Inc.

DUNCAN PHYFE
(1768–1854), New York

8.
Pair of Lyre-Back Side Chairs, 1816

Mahogany with ebony, 32¼ in. high

RECORDED: *cf.* Jeanne Vibert Sloane, "A
Duncan Phyfe bill and the furniture it
documents," in *The Magazine Antiques*,
CXXXI (May 1987), p. 1109

The lyre-back klismos chair was one of the
most popular forms of the Neo-Classical
period. Although most have been
attributed to Duncan Phyfe, they must
certainly also have been made by a number
of other cabinetmakers in New York and
possibly elsewhere. These chairs (one
illustrated), two from an original set of
twelve, ten of which are now in The
Brooklyn Museum, are documented as the
work of Phyfe by an invoice he rendered
to the Philadelphia businessman, Charles
N. Bancker (1777–1869), on January 4,
1816: "12 Mahogany Chairs @ $22 . . .
$264." An accompanying sketch by Phyfe
shows a similar chair with a carved crest
rail, as well as a rare variant of his familiar
curule chair, and gives prices for making
them either with caned seats and cushions,
or with the upholstered slip seats with
which these chairs were supplied. The fact
that these chairs were made for a client in
Philadelphia demonstrates the growth of
Phyfe's reputation and the widespread
distribution of his work.

The Brooklyn Museum, New York, H.
Randolph Lever Fund

9.
Portrait of John Townsend McCoun,
about 1813–15

Oil on wood panel, 25⅝ x 21⅛ in.
(sight size)

EXHIBITED: Hirschl & Adler Galleries,
New York, 1972–73, *Faces and Places,
Changing Images of 19th Century America,*
no. 50 illus. // Hirschl & Adler Galleries,
New York, 1982, *American Art from the
Colonial and Federal Periods,* no. 59 illus.

EX COLL.: Mrs. Angelica Dunham, New
Haven, Connecticut, until 1985; to
[Hirschl & Adler Galleries, 1972–85]; to
private collection, New York, 1985–91

Jarvis was born in England, but grew up in
Philadelphia, where he worked for the
painter and engraver Edward Savage. At
the end of his apprenticeship, Jarvis moved
to New York, where, rising to prominence
as a portrait painter, he soon received what
became his most important and successful
commission: a series of dramatic full-
length portraits of military heroes from
the War of 1812, executed for New York
City Hall (see p. 22).

John Townsend McCoun (1803–
1861), first son and second child of
Samuel and Elizabeth (Townsend)
McCoun, was born in New York. In 1823
he went with his father to Troy, New
York, where he married Angelica Rachel
Dowd Lane, daughter of Derick and
Angelica (Van Rensselaer) Lane, on
September 9, 1828. In Troy he joined the
mercantile firm of T. McCoun & Co., and
was one of the originators of the Second
Street Presbyterian Church, and the First
Troy Young Men's Association, a fore-
runner of the Troy Public Library. He was
a Director of the Mutual Insurance Com-
pany and Troy Gas & Light Company.

10.

Neo-Classical Single-Pedestal Drop-Leaf Breakfast Table, New York, possibly workshop of Duncan Phyfe (1768–1854), about 1805–15

Mahogany, with brass animal paw toe caps and castors, and lion-head pulls, 28½ x 39 x 23¼ in. (46½ x 39 in. with leaves extended)

Among the most successful and characteristic forms of furniture of the Classical Revival period is the single-pedestal breakfast, or library, table. An outstanding example of New York craftsmanship and style, this table bears all the attributes associated with the workshop of Duncan Phyfe, or the style that he helped to create in New York in the early years of the nineteenth century. Distinguishing features are the carefully selected and richly figured mahogany, the well carved reeded urn and shaft, the bold waterleaf carving on the splayed legs, the cast brass animal paw toe caps, and the boldly pressed lion-head drawer pulls, which retain traces of their original gilding.

11.

Neo-Classical Drop-Leaf Breakfast Table, New York, about 1815

Mahogany, with gilt brass lion-head pulls and castors, 28½ x 36 x 25¼ in. (36 x 45½ in. with both leaves fully extended)

This well-proportioned table, incorporating double elliptic drop leaves, boldly modeled lion-head pulls, and the unusual detail of tapered fluted panels on the legs, which terminate in the original brass castors, is one of the most characteristic designs of the early Neo-Classical period in New York. Although it is of a form and style often ascribed to the workshop of Duncan Phyfe (1768–1864), a few unusual details, including the shape of the reeded legs and the fluted panels below (see no. 1), relate to details seen on various pieces by Charles-Honoré Lannuier.

JOHN WESLEY JARVIS
(1780–1840)

12.
Portrait of a Man, about 1815–20

Oil on canvas, 35½ x 29½ in. (sight size)
Signed (at lower left): J. W. Jarvis

It has been variously suggested that this is
a self-portrait or a portrait of an actor.
While it does not appear to relate to any
known likenesses of actors of the early
nineteenth century, it does bear more than
a casual resemblance to the supposed self-
portrait as a sailor in a striped shirt
included in Jarvis' full-length portrait of
Commodore Oliver Hazard Perry of 1816
in City Hall, New York (see: Harold E.
Dickson, *John Wesley Jarvis, American Painter*
[1949], no. 67 illus.). In its dashing and
informal attitude it ranks as an unusual
and spontaneous example of early
Romantic portraiture in the United
States. As a signed work, it is also
extremely unusual in Jarvis' oeuvre.

JOHN WESLEY JARVIS
(1780–1840)

13a.
Portrait of Katherine W. Andrews,
about 1820

13b.
Portrait of David Andrews, about 1820

Each, oil on canvas, 33¼ x 26 in.

EX COLL.: by descent in the family of the
sitters, until 1984

Jarvis was one of the best portrait painters
active in the United States during the
Neo-Classical period. Based essentially in
New York, he often travelled in search of
commissions to New Orleans, Richmond,
Virginia, Washington, D.C., and Charleston, South Carolina. In contrast to the
tightly realistic likenesses done by the
painting firm of Waldo & Jewett (see
nos. 28a and 28b), Jarvis' portraits display
a dashing brush stroke that endow them
with a striking immediacy.

David Andrews (1780–1837) of
Newburgh, New York, married Katherine
Walsh (1785–1829) in 1805. Details of the
costumes suggest a date for the portraits
of about 1820.

14.

Secrétaire à Abattant, New York, probably
workshop of Duncan Phyfe (1768–1854),
about 1815

Rosewood, mahogany paint-grained
rosewood, secondary woods partially
painted verde antique and gilded, brass
die-stamped and string inlay, ormolu
mounts, mirror plate, leather writing
surface, and marble top, 60⅛ x 39⅛ x 20 in.

RECORDED: *cf.* Robert C. Smith, "The
furniture of Anthony G. Quervelle, Part
IV: Some case pieces," in *The Magazine
Antiques*, CV (Jan. 1974), p. 101 fig. 1 //
Hirschl & Adler Galleries, New York,
The State of the Arts (1990), pp. 78–79
fig. 7.7 in color

This *secrétaire à abbatant,* inspired by plates
published by Pierre de la Mésangère in his
Collection des Meubles et Objets de Goût, which
appeared serially in Paris between 1796
and 1830, is a recent discovery and relates
closely to four other examples, all
different in such details as the design of
the feet, the selection and arrangement of
the ormolu mounts, and the composition
of the interiors. They are, however, clearly
the work of a single cabinetmaking shop.
Although previously ascribed to Philadelphia, they are now seen to relate much
more closely to the most sophisticated
production of Duncan Phyfe and would
appear to rank among his finest pieces of
French-style furniture.

15.

*Pair of Neo-Classical Figural Card
Tables*, New York, manner of Charles-
Honoré Lannuier (1779–1819; active in
the United States, 1803–1819), about 1815

Rosewood, secondary woods painted verde
antique and gilded, with brass die-stamped
and string inlay and castors, 29½ x 36¼ x
18⅛ in. (open: 36¼ x 36¼ in.)

EX COLL.: private collection, 1970–91

This pair of card tables is close in style to
a group of furniture with winged female
figural supports (see no. 16) stamped or
labelled by, or attributed to, the French
emigré cabinetmaker Charles-Honoré
Lannuier. Although these elegantly
composed tables bear all the earmarks of a
Lannuier style, they vary in subtle details
of design and carving from other known
Lannuier tables of this type, and it has

been suggested that they are by one of his
New York contemporaries, very possibly
Duncan Phyfe (1768–1854). Indeed, just
as Lannuier is known to have produced
furniture that is seemingly purely Phyfe in
style (see no. 4), so must Phyfe, Michael
Allison, and others have sought to meet
the competition of Lannuier's figural
pieces by making a line of such furniture
of their own.

CHARLES-HONORE LANNUIER
(1779–1819; active in the United States, 1803–1819), New York

16.
Pier Table, with Winged Female Caryatid Supports, 1816–19

Mahogany, secondary woods painted verde antique and gilded, with brass die-stamped and string inlay, ebony, ormolu mounts, mirror plate, and white marble top, 35¼ x 48½ x 20 in.
Stamped (with two separate steel dyes, [1] and [2], twice at the top of the inside of each front leg): [1] H. LANNUIER/NEW-YORK/[2] JACOB
Labelled (with engraved, bilingual, cheval-glass label, attached to the inside of the rear rail, below the marble top): Hre. Lannuier,/Cabinet Maker from Paris/Kips [*sic:* Keeps] is [*sic:* his] whare house [*sic:* warehouse] of/new fashion fourniture [*sic*]/Broad Street No 60, New-York./Hre. Lannuier,/Ebeniste de Paris,/Tient Fabrique &c/Magasin de Meubles/les plus a la mode,/New-York.

Although the earliest furniture made by Charles-Honoré Lannuier in New York reflects the French styles of the Consulat and Directoire (see no. 1) and a style usually associated with his principal competitor, Duncan Phyfe (see no. 4), his mature work, exemplified by this elaborate pier, or console, table, relied heavily on the forms and style of the First Empire, a knowledge of which he undoubtedly gained both through personal exposure before he left Paris in 1803, and through the designs published by Pierre de la Mésangère in *Collection des Meubles et Objects de Goût*, which appeared in Paris from 1796 to 1830.

Handsomely composed around two winged female caryatid supports, the table demonstrates Lannuier's unique mastery of the French idiom in the United States. Using the finest of mahogany veneers, carved, gilded, and painted verde antique winged caryatids and hock-footed animal supports, ebony, brass die-stamped and string inlay, imported French ormolu mounts of the best quality, mirror plate, and a white marble top, the table emerges as not only one of the artist's own supreme achievements, but also as one of the landmark pieces in the history of cabinet-making in the United States. It relates closely to a pier table from the Pierrepont family (The Brooklyn Museum, New York; see: Donald C. Pierce, "New York Furniture in The Brooklyn Museum," in *The Magazine Antiques*, CXVI [May 1979], p. 1001 pl. VIII), a pair of pier tables from the home of the prominent New York merchant Nathanial Prime, whose residence was at 1 Broadway (Museum of the

City of New York; see: *The Magazine Antiques*, LXVI [Nov. 1954], p. 404 illus.), and a center table (private collection, New York; see: Wendy A. Cooper, *In Praise of America* [National Gallery of Art, Washington, D.C., 1980], p. 244 pl. 48), as well as to a group of figural card tables, of which particularly distinguished examples are in the The Albany Institute of History and Art, New York; The Valentine Museum, Richmond, Virginia; and The Metropolitan Museum of Art, New York.

Twice stamped with a typically French *estampille* with Lannuier's name, the table also bears the third and last form of label used by Lannuier, the so-called bilingual cheval-glass label, which he began using only in 1816, thus placing this table within the brief period between then and his premature death in 1819.

This table, the original mate to which is in a New York private collection, is said to have been made for Armand de Balbi (1778–1838), who was born in Paris and moved to New York at the age of twenty-four. It descended in his family until 1988.

The Jacob stamp, apparently identifying a member of the prominent family of French cabinetmakers active in Paris from the late eighteenth century until well into the twentieth, must have been added attendant to an early restoration, probably when the table was taken to Paris, presumably during the second quarter of the nineteenth century.

After BARON AXEL LEONHARD
KLINCKOWSTROM
(active in the United States 1818–1820)

Engraved by
CARL FREDERIK AKRELL
(1779–1868)

17.
Brodway-gatan och Radhuset i Newyork,
a plate from *Bref om de Forenta Staterne,*
Stockholm, 1824

Aquatint, 11¼ x 18½ in.

RECORDED: *cf.* I. N. Phelps Stokes, *The
Iconography of Manhattan Island* (1915–26),
III, pp. 563–64 pl. 85 // *cf.* Gloria Gilda
Deak, *Picturing America 1497–1899* (1988),
no. 310

An air of serenity and elegance pervades
this view of lower Broadway, aided in no
small part by a uniformly classical
cityscape. From the imposing Doric
columns supporting the portico of St.
Paul's Chapel on the left to the imposing
facade of New York's new City Hall (see
no. 24), a sense of coherent order informs
this portrait of what was then the city's
most fashionable residential quarter.

The author of this charming scene
was the Swedish aristocrat Baron Axel
Leonhard Klinckowstrom, who spent three
years in the United States gathering
material for a travel account of the new
republic. In 1824 he published his *Letters
from the United States,* whose text was
supplemented by aquatints executed by his
talented countryman, the master engraver
Carl Frederik Akrell.

Brodway-gatan och Radhuset i Newyork.

STEPHEN RICHARD
(active 1802–1839), New York

18.
Presentation Ewer and Salver, about 1825

Silver
Ewer: 13¼ in. high
Inscribed (on side, right of spout):
THE/Phenix Bank/of NEW YORK
to/Charles Bancroft Esqr.
Salver: 1¹⁵⁄₁₆ x 17¾ in.
Signed: (with engraved signature, on the bottom): S. Richard/Maker/New York
Inscribed (in the center): THE/Phenix Bank/of NEW YORK to/Charles Bancroft Esqr.

RECORDED: Merrill Denison, *Canada's First Bank*, I (1966), p. 78, as by L. [*sic*] Richard of New York.

EXHIBITED: The Museum of Fine Arts, Houston, Texas; Minneapolis Institute of Arts, Minnesota; and The Metropolitan Museum of Art, New York, 1987–88, *Marks of Achievement — Four Centuries of American Presentation Silver*, pp. 92–93 no. 103

Stylistically, the silver that Stephen Richard produced during his long career spans the various phases of the Classical Revival (see no. 2). Unusually refined for New York silver of this period, this ewer and salver combine cast and repoussé ornament to produce a work of considerable power and distinction that rivals the production of London silversmith Paul Storr and his contemporaries. In place of the customary touch mark found on silver, Richard usually signed his works, with an engraved script signature, as shown here.

The presentation inscription commemorates a relationship between the New Yorker Charles Bancroft, who moved to Montreal in 1815 to join the banking firm of Gates and Nephew, and the Phenix Bank in New York (see no. 25), with which he continued to do business. An identical ewer and salver bearing a similar inscription to Bancroft's partner, Horatio Gates, is said to remain in the possession of Gates' descendants in Hamilton, Ontario, Canada.

19.

Cellarette with Sphinx Supports,
New York, about 1815–20

Rosewood, ebony, secondary woods
painted verde antique and gilded, with
brass die-stamped and string inlay and
castors, and ormolu mounts, 30 x 34⅛ x
25 in.

This cellarette is closely related to another
at the Yale University Art Gallery, New
Haven, Connecticut. When the Yale
cellarette was exhibited in *Classical America
1815–1845* at The Newark Museum, New
Jersey, in 1963, it was attributed to
Charles-Honoré Lannuier and dated to
about 1815–19. In the more than twenty-
five years that have elapsed since the
Newark exhibition, more sophisticated
scholarship and the appearance of
additional examples have added signifi-
cantly to our understanding of this period.
Like the pair of card tables with winged
female figural supports (see no. 15), this
extraordinary tour-de-force of American
Neo-Classical design was made in New
York, undoubtedly by one of Lannuier's
skillful and innovative competitors.

The Manney Collection

Attributed to DUNCAN PHYFE
(1768–1854), New York

20.
Card Table with Columnar Support,
about 1820

Rosewood, partially painted verde antique
and gilded, with brass castors and die-
stamped and string inlay, and ormolu
mount, 29⅛ x 36 x 18 in. (open: 36 x 36 in.)

Essentially a New York interpretation of
the French Restauration style, this
fashionable table also shows the influence
of the Regency period in England; it
exhibits a blending of forms and sources
that is characteristic of much American
Neo-Classical furniture. A center table
with nearly identical feet and central
columnar support is at "Edgewater,"
Barrytown, New York.

   A pair of tables of similar form and
design, but more purely in the aesthetic of
the French Restauration, is in The
Metropolitan Museum of Art (see: The
Metropolitan Museum of Art, New York,
*19th Century America, Furniture and Other
Decorative Arts* [1970], fig. 71).

ASHER B. DURAND
(1796–1886)

21a.
Musidora, 1825

Line engraving, 15⅝ x 10¹⁄₁₆ in.

RECORDED: *cf.* The Grolier Club,
Engraved Work of Asher B. Durand (1895),
no. 236 // *cf.* David McNeeley Stauffer,
American Engravers upon Copper and Steel
(1907), no. 683

Engraved by ASHER B. DURAND
(1796–1886)

After JOHN VANDERLYN
(1775–1852)

21b.
Ariadne, 1835

Seven line engravings, 14³⁄₁₆ x 17¼ in.
Six of seven proof states, plus the
final state

RECORDED: *cf.* The Grolier Club,
Engraved Work of Asher B. Durand (1895),
no. 237 // *cf.* David McNeeley Stauffer,
American Engravers upon Copper and Steel
(1907), no. 682

EX COLL.: the artist; to Mr. Charles
Henry Hart; Mrs. Henry C. Sturgis

Asher B. Durand was one of a number of notable nineteenth-century American painters who began their careers at the side of a printing press. At the age of seventeen Durand apprenticed with the engraver Peter Maverick, but soon thereafter set his sights upon higher artistic pursuits. He was among the first artists to introduce the nude to the American public as a subject for the fine arts, a distinction which not only put him decades ahead of his peers and public taste, but which virtually guaranteed the commercial failure of his two most accomplished engravings, *Musidora* and *Ariadne.*

Musidora, engraved after Durand's own design in 1825, was inspired by a poem by the Scottish poet James Thomson entitled *The Seasons.* The figure is derived from an ancient statue of Venus reproduced in an illustrated eighteenth-century publication by Bartolemeo Cavaceppi devoted to classical sculpture and bas relief.

By the time Durand completed *Ariadne,* ten years later, he was recognized as the preeminent engraver of his day. The composition is based upon a painting completed in 1812 by John Vanderlyn, purchased by Durand in 1831, and now in the Pennsylvania Academy of the Fine Arts, Philadelphia. According to John Durand, the artist's son, publication was undertaken as a labor of love and the print is considered by many today to be the finest example of the engraver's art produced in this country during the nineteenth century.

Determined to devote himself full-time to painting, Durand left *Ariadne* as his valediction to the graphic arts. The *New York Mirror* noted in May 1836: "Perhaps he thinks he cannot go beyond his Ariadne. No one else can." The only other set of proofs extant is in the New York Public Library.

First State of Eight

Eighth and Final State

NEW YORK FROM WEEHAWK.

To Thomas Dixon Esq.r this Plate is respectfully Inscribed by his Obliged Serv.t Will.m G. Wall.

Painted and Published by Will.m G. Wall, New York 1823.

NEW YORK FROM HEIGHTS NEAR BROOKLYN.

To Thomas Dixon Esq.r this Plate is respectfully Inscribed by his Obliged Serv.t Will.m G. Wall.

Painted and Published by Will.m G. Wall, New York 1823.

After WILLIAM GUY WALL
(1792–after 1863)

Engraved by JOHN HILL
(1770–1850)

22a.
New York From Weehawk, 1823

Hand-colored aquatint with engraving,
15¾ x 24¼ in.
First state of three

RECORDED: *cf*. Richard J. Koke, *A Check-list of the American Engravings of John Hill (1770–1850)* (1961), no. 95 // *cf*. Gloria Gilda Deak, *Picturing America 1497–1899* (1988), no. 336

22b.
New York From Heights Near Brooklyn, 1823

Hand-colored aquatint with engraving,
15½ x 24 in.
First state of three

RECORDED: *cf*. Richard J. Koke, *A Check-list of the American Engravings of John Hill (1770–1850)* (1961), no. 96 // *cf*. Gloria Gilda Deak, *Picturing America 1497–1899* (1988), no. 335

Perhaps the finest of the early nineteenth-century engraved views of New York is this companion pair engraved by John Hill after the watercolor drawings by William Guy Wall now in the collection of The Metropolitan Museum of Art, New York.

Dublin-born Wall first arrived in America in 1818, settling in New York City. In the summer of 1820 he went on a tour of the Hudson, compiling a series of sketches which would later be engraved in aquatint by John Hill as the celebrated collection of views entitled *The Hudson River Portfolio*. Three years later a notice appeared in the *Commercial Advertiser* for June 26, 1823, advertising the continued collaboration of the two artists in the publication of this elegant pair of views:

"Mr. Wall has been induced ... to offer to the patronage of the public, two *aqua tinta* engravings of this City ... in the choice of which points of view, he has been determined by their affording the most favorable view of the city, and conveying the most correct impression of the beauties of the Bay, and the surrounding scenery. Every exertion will be made to obtain the best possible execution of these engravings, an artist of known and approved skill having been engaged for the purpose."

23.
Piano, New York, about 1825–31

Works by Firth, Hall & Browning, New York
Rosewood, secondary woods partially painted and gilded, with brass and wood string inlay, gilt brass on lead moldings, ivory keys, gilt brass medallion, and piano works, 76 x 45¼ (53½ overall at cornice) x 24 in.
Signed (with stencilled name, above the keyboard): MADE BY/FIRTH, HALL & BROWNING/358/PEARL STREET/NEW YORK

RECORDED: *cf.* Oscar P. Fitzgerald, *Three Centuries of American Furniture* (1982), p. 122 fig. VI-24

EX COLL.: Walter P. Chrysler, Jr., New York; to his estate, until 1990

The enjoyment of music was a favorite American pastime in the early years of the Republic (see no. 90) and created a demand for English- and European-trained instrument makers, a considerable number of whom came to this country at the beginning of the nineteenth century. Eminent among them was the English-born John Firth (1789–1864), who arrived in the United States in 1810 and went into business with William Hall (1796–1874) in 1822. The New York directories list them together as a "music store" at 358 Pearl Street from 1823 to 1831. Thomas Browning joined the firm in 1825 as a "piano-forte maker" and remained with Firth and Hall at various addresses until 1831.

Whether the cases used by Firth, Hall & Browning and other fine instrument makers of the period were made in their own shops or by such established cabinetmakers as the celebrated Duncan Phyfe remains unknown. Nevertheless, the case of this upright piano, still at this time an unusual form, ranks with the best furniture produced in New York in this period. It is distinguished by heavy brass string inlay outlining panels of richly colored and figured rosewood veneers, crisply cast ormolu mounts and gilt brass moldings, and a striking centerpiece of a pleated silk sunburst emanating from a gilt brass passion flower and surrounded by carved angel heads and wings. The characteristic stencilled signature above the keyboard is preserved in perfect condition, protected as it must often have been by the closed lid of the piano, giving a hint of the original appearance of other stencilled ornament of this period that has been less well treated.

The design of the case demonstrates a skillful interpretation of French and English sources found in the fashionable pattern books of the day, most specifically in Pierre de la Mésangère's *Collection des Meubles et Objets de Goût,* published serially in Paris from 1796 to 1830.

ALEXANDER JACKSON DAVIS
(1803–1892)

24.
City Hall, New York, 1826

Pen and ink and watercolor on paper,
13¹³/₁₆ x 18¼ in.
Signed, dated, and inscribed (at lower
left): Drawn by A. J. Davis, Aug. 1826; (at
lower center): CITY HALL, NEW YORK,
Length 276 feet, Breadth 105 Height 51 —
including attic 65 feet.

EXHIBITED: Art Commission of the City
of New York, City Hall, 1984, *On City
Hall, In City Hall*, p. 1

EX COLL.: Mr. and Mrs. Frederick
Deming Sherman, Brooklyn, New York,
about 1900; by descent in the family; to
sale 5190, Sotheby's, New York, May 31,

1984, vol. II, no. 85 illus.; to private
collection

Completed in 1812, the third and current
New York City Hall is one of the most
elaborate architectural monuments of the
early nineteenth century in the United
States. A successful blend of French Louis
XVI and American Federal styles, it was
designed by the French-born architect
Joseph François Mangin and his American
collaborator, John McComb, Jr. City
Hall's elaborately ornamented interior (see
p. 22) became a showcase for the work of
some of America's best portraitists of the
period, among them John Trumbull and
John Wesley Jarvis, as well as the finest

artisans of the day, including the French
emigré cabinetmaker Charles-Honoré
Lannuier (see no. 4).

Trained as a draftsman, lithographer,
and architect, Davis designed many public
buildings, including the state capitols of
Indiana, Connecticut, and North
Carolina; indeed he dominated the field of
architecture in America for more than
thirty years. This watercolor view of New
York City Hall was executed early in
Davis' career, before he established himself
as an architect.

Private collection

CHARLES BURTON
(active in the United States, 1819–1842)

25.
Phenix Bank, Wall Street, 1831

Sepia wash and pencil on paper,
2¾ x 3½ in. (image size)
Signed, dated, and inscribed (at lower
left): C Burton Delt.; (at lower right):
Phenix Bank, Wall St/1831

RECORDED: *cf.* I. N. Phelps Stokes, *The
Iconography of Manhattan Island* (1918, reprint
1967), III, pp. 594, 596 pl. 11, 597

EX COLL.: commissioned by George
Melksham Bourne, New York, 1831; James
Smillie, engraver, New York; by descent to
his grandsons, Ralph and James C.
Smillie, New Jersey, until 1979; to
[Hirschl & Adler Galleries, New York]; to
private collection, New York, in 1979

This view of Wall Street is one of a group
of thirty-eight drawings of various New
York scenes that Charles Burton made for
George Melksham Bourne, who issued a
series of engravings based on them in
1831. At the center of the drawing is the
Doric-columned Phenix Bank, clearly
inspired by Greek prototypes, surrounded
on either side by buildings in Italianate
and American Federal styles. Burton's
interest was not limited to depicting the
architecture of New York; he also
observed the life around him, recording
different seasons, elegant carriages, and, as
here, the latest in both men's and women's
fashions.

Private collection

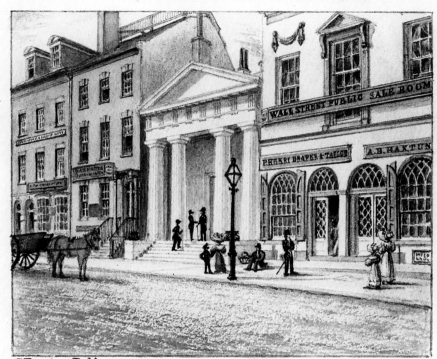

THOMAS COLE
(1801–1848)

26.
Mountain Sunrise, 1826

Oil on panel, 18⅛ x 24⅜ in. (sight size)
Signed and dated (at center left):
T. Cole/1826

EXHIBITED: Wadsworth Atheneum, Hartford, Connecticut, and Whitney Museum of American Art, New York, 1948–49, *Thomas Cole, 1801–1848, One Hundred Years Later, a Loan Exhibition*, p. 19 no. 5, lent by Mr. and Mrs. Alfred H. Barr, Jr., New York // The Art Institute of Chicago, 1949, *The Hudson River School and the Early American Landscape Tradition*, no. 60 illus. // National Collection of Fine Arts, Washington, D.C., 1966, *American Landscape: A Changing Frontier*, p. 3 in

checklist, lent by a private collection, New York // Memorial Art Gallery of the University of Rochester, New York; Munson-Williams-Proctor Institute, Utica, New York; Albany Institute of History and Art, New York; and Whitney Museum of American Art, New York, 1969, *Thomas Cole*, pp. 22–23 no. 6, 61 no. 6 illus., lent anonymously

EX COLL.: John Ludlow Morton, New York; by descent in the family, until 1913; to [W. L. A. Galleries, New York, in 1913]; [Newhouse Galleries, New York, by 1943]; to Mr. and Mrs. Alfred H. Barr, Jr., New York, in 1944, until at least 1969

More than any other artist, Thomas Cole was instrumental in establishing landscape painting as a viable alternative to portrait

or figure painting in America. Considered the founder of the Hudson River School, he painted specific locales, particularly in and around his beloved Catskill Mountains, as well as moral and religious allegories set within grand-scale, imaginary landscape or architectural contexts. Cole took a sketching trip up the Hudson River for the first time in 1825, and the paintings that resulted from that expedition, including the present work, are among his earliest mature landscapes. In these early paintings, and indeed throughout his career, Cole celebrated the sublime grandeur of the American landscape, where the subject of the picture was nature itself, free of the more purely topographical concerns of his contemporaries.

THOMAS DOUGHTY
(1793–1856)

27.
View on Lake George, 1829

Oil on wood panel, 11⅞₆ x 15⅞ in.
Signed and dated (at lower center):
Doughty/1829; incised (on the back):
D.L.B.

EX COLL.: W. Nutting

Doughty depicted specific locations in his
landscapes of the late 1820s, but, as time
went on, they became increasingly
idealized, following the tradition of the
European classical landscape. However,
while European artists such as Claude
Lorrain and Salvator Rosa used landscape
as the setting for religious or mythological
subjects, Doughty chose to depict commonplace hunters and anglers which were
more in keeping with the democratic
ideals of the United States.

SAMUEL LOVETT WALDO
(1783–1861)
and
WILLIAM JEWETT
(1789/90–1874)

28a.
Portrait of a Woman, 1831

28b.
Portrait of a Man, 1831

Each, oil on wood panel, 33 x 25¼ in.
Each, signed, dated, and inscribed (with a
stamp, on the back): WALDO &
JEWETT/1831/NEW YORK

During a period when portrait painting
still commanded the full attention of the
majority of artists active in America, the
painting partnership of Waldo & Jewett
appears to have been outstandingly
successful. Working together from about
1818 to 1854, they very capably and
realistically documented the appearance of
several generations of New Yorkers. Their
characteristic stamp on the back of each of
these portraits precisely dates them, but
the identity of the subjects remains
unknown.

WILLIAM PAGE
(1811–1885)

29.
Young Girl in Pink, about 1835–36

Oil on canvas, 36½ x 29 in.
Signed and inscribed (at lower left): W
Page; (on inside edge of original stretcher,
now mounted on back of new stretcher):
OWNED. BY. D. LONG.

Born in Albany, New York, William Page
moved with his family to New York City
when he was nine. He received his early
artistic training there during the
mid-1820s from the painters James
Herring and Samuel F. B. Morse. He
became a regular exhibitor at the National
Academy of Design, and in 1836 was
elected a full member of the Academy.
Reviews of the works he exhibited there
were extremely favorable, citing his fine
drawing and use of rich, clear color as
particularly unusual and appealing.

The sitter of this portrait has not
been identified, but it can be dated on
stylistic grounds to the mid-1830s. The
young girl, who is probably six or seven
years old, wears a morning costume
typical of the Classical Revival period:
full-skirted dress with front-and-side
pleats, off-the-shoulder short sleeves with
close gathers at the shoulder, "drooping"
cross-over bodice, high, Empire waistline,
enormous hat, and simple hairstyle.

The portrait retains its original
Greek Revival frame.

Attributed to DUNCAN PHYFE
(1768–1854), New York

30.
Pair of Double Curule Stools,
about 1835–40

Rosewood, with brass castors, 16⅛ x
23¼ x 19 in.

EX COLL.: Maurice P. Van Buren, New
York, and his estate, until 1987; [Hirschl
& Adler Galleries, New York]; to private
collection, New York, until 1990

Although the name Duncan Phyfe is most
often associated with the tasteful reeded
furniture that his workshop produced in
the early years of the nineteenth century,
his shop is also known to have worked in a
wide range of styles, from the more purely
classical and delicate lines of Sheraton and
Hepplewhite designs to the heavier adaptations of French Restauration and later
English Regency forms.

      This unusual pair of double curule
stools can be attributed to Phyfe based on
the similarity of style, quality, and
construction to a well-documented suite of

furniture commissioned in 1837 for the
residence of the prominent New York
attorney Samuel A. Foot, which is now in
the Greek Revival Parlor at The Metropolitan Museum of Art (see: The
Metropolitan Museum of Art, New York,
1970, *19th Century America, Furniture and
Other Decorative Arts,* p. 79 illus.).

      The stools are nearly identical to a
pair of round stools, also in The
Metropolitan Museum of Art, that were
part of the furnishings of "Plum Point,"
New Windsor, near Newburgh, New
York, which was built about 1838 by
Philip Alexander Ver Planck.

      Like much American Neo-Classical
furniture, the form of these stools was
probably based on the designs published in
Paris in the late 1820s in Pierre de la
Mésangère's *Collection des Meubles et Objets de
Goût.* They are distinguished by their
strong, architectural lines and the rich
color and grain of their rosewood veneers.

CYRUS LANCASTER
(1802–1862) of JAMES WILSON & SONS, Albany, New York

Retailed by S. WOOD & SONS, New York

31.
Wilson's Thirteen-Inch Terrestrial Globe,
1835

Mahogany, pine, brass and other metals, paper, and miscellaneous materials, 18¼ in. high (including stand)
Printed (on the globe): Wilson's/New American Thirteen Inch/TERRESTRIAL GLOBE/Exhibiting with the greatest possible Accuracy/THE POSITIONS of the PRINCIPAL KNOWN PLACES/of the EARTH/With the Tracks of Various Circumnavigators together with New Discoveries and Political Alterations down to The present PERIOD 1835/BY C. LANCASTER. ALBANY ST. NY/S. Wood & Sons Agents N.York

Although largely self-taught in geography and the techniques of engraving, James Wilson, America's first commercial globe maker, produced terrestrial and celestial globes that were accurate, beautiful, and a commercial success. In 1818 he moved from Vermont to establish a manufactory in Albany, New York, trading as James Wilson and Company (1819–1822), and then as James Wilson & Sons (1822–1835). His sons, John and Samuel, who had managed the business in Albany, both died in 1833. Cyrus Lancaster, an employee since 1826, married Samuel's widow and continued making Wilson's Globes with the addition of his own name until about 1850.

LOUIS A. SMITH
(active about 1841–1845), New York

32.
Barometer, 1843

Mahogany, brass, copperplate engraving on paper, mirror plate, and various materials, 38 in. high
Signed (on the dial): L.A. SMITH.

Barometers of American manufacture are exceedingly rare. This one, which follows the design of the familiar "banjo" shape of English barometers, is signed by L.A. Smith of New York.

There are two *Lewis* Smiths listed in the New York directories for this period. In 1841–42 Lewis A. Smith, "Jeweller," is listed at 87 Eleventh St. "n[ear] . . . 5th [Avenue]." In the 1842–43, 1843–44, and 1844–45 directories Lewis S. Smith, "Barometer maker," is listed on 22nd Street, "n[ear] . . . 2nd [Avenue]." It is likely that both Smiths are actually the *Louis A.* Smith who made this and other barometers that bear his name. An old piece of newspaper inserted behind the mirrored panel at the bottom of the case is dated 1843.

NICOLINO CALYO
(1799–1884)

33a.
View of the Great Fire in New York, 1837

Gouache on paper, 11 x 15⅞ in.
Signed, dated, and inscribed (at lower
left): N. Calyo f. N. York 1837; (on the
back, by an unidentified hand): View of
the Great Fire in New York Decr 16th &
17th 1835./as seen from the top of the
new Building of the Bank of America
corner of Wall & William St.; (on an old
label, by an unidentified hand): Incendie
de new york/16/17 X [*sic*] 1835/Dessine
d'apres nature

33b.
*View of the Ruins after the Great Fire in
New York*, 1837

Gouache on paper, 11¼ x 15½ in.
Signed, dated, and inscribed (at lower
left): N. Calyo N. York 1837; (on the
back, by an unidentified hand): View of
the Ruins after the Great Fire in New
York Decr 16th & 17th 1835./as seen from
Exchange Place.

RECORDED: Kennedy Galleries, New
York, *The Kennedy Quarterly: Early American
Views 1700–1880* (1963), pp. 196 no. 311
illus., 197 nos. 311 and 312 // Margaret
Sloane Patterson, "Nicolino Calyo and his
Paintings of the Great Fire of New York,
December 16th and 17th, 1835," in *The
American Art Journal*, XIV (Spring 1982),
pp. 4 fig. 1, 13 fig. 13, 14–15 // Henry
Lee, "The Most Awful Calamity," in
Seaport, 24 (Fall 1990), p. 32 illus. (*View of
the Ruins* only)

EXHIBITED: Baltimore Museum of Art,
and The Metropolitan Museum of Art,
New York, 1967, *American Paintings and
Historical Prints from the Middendorf Collection*,
pp. 28–29 nos. 17a and 17b illus. //
Hirschl & Adler Galleries, New York,
1969, *The American Scene*, nos. 7a and 7b

EX COLL.: [Kennedy Galleries, New York,
by 1963]; to Mr. and Mrs. J. William
Middendorf, II, New York, 1963–69; to
[Hirschl & Adler Galleries, New York,
1969]; to private collection, 1969–88

The Neapolitan painter Nicolino Calyo
arrived in New York late in 1835, just in
time to witness the worst conflagration
that the city or the nation had ever
experienced. As Margaret Sloane Patterson
noted, the series of views that resulted
from his experience follows in the
tradition of paintings of eruptions of
Vesuvius executed by Calyo and other
Neapolitan artists in the late eighteenth
and early nineteenth centuries.

The Great Fire of New York began
on the night of December 16, 1835, and
throughout the next fifteen hours
destroyed virtually the entire business
district of the city, including the
Merchants' Exchange, the Post Office, and
more than half the insurance companies.
Seen in the first view at far right are The
Fulton Fire Insurance Company, housed in
a Greek Revival building, and the old
Merchant's Exchange with its classically-
inspired, Ionic-columned facade. The
second view depicts the ruins of the
Italianate Garden Street Church on the
far left.

Other versions of these views, similar
in composition, served as the basis for
William J. Bennett's well-known aquatints
published the same year.

JAMES THOMSON
(active 1834–1841), New York

34.
Pair of Oval Covered Vegetable Dishes,
1837–38

Silver, 6⅛ x 13⁷⁄₁₆ x 10⁵⁄₁₆ in.
Marked (on the bottom of each): Jas
Thomson/NEW YORK/1838
Marked (on the rim of the cover and the
dish of one): H; (on the rim of the cover
and the dish of the other): T
Engraved (on the side of each cover):
Presented by/The Manhattan Gas Light
Compy./TO/Lambert Suydam
Esqr . ./New York 22d Feby 1837

EX COLL.: Lambert Suydam, New York

Although entire services of silver hollow-
ware were commonplace adornments of the
great homes in England during the

Regency period, such services appear to
have been extremely rare in American
silver at this time. The stamped letters
"H" and "T" that appear on each of these
covered vegetable dishes may imply that
they were at one time part of a very large
and elaborate presentation service. Their
extremely fine quality, very heavy weight,
and carefully molded borders and handles
place them among the finest pieces of
American silver of the Neo-Classical
period. The handles of the covers are
removable to make a second pair of
vegetable dishes. The *rocaille* engraving
which surrounds the presentation
inscriptions shows that by the late 1830s
Rococo tendencies were beginning to
assert themselves within the more rigid
stylistic conventions of the Classical
Revival.

James Thomson was the successor to
William Thomson, a distinguished silversmith active in New York during the years
1815–34.

Attributed to DUNCAN PHYFE
(1768–1854), New York

35.
Bonheur du Jour, about 1835–40

Mahogany, secondary woods partially
marbleized, with marble, baize writing
surface, mirror plate, and brass
escutcheons, 68½ x 36½ x 20¼ in.

Relying heavily on large expanses of richly
figured "matchbook" veneers for ornamentation, this *bonheur du jour,* or small
secretary bookcase, is close in style to a
suite of furniture (The Metropolitan
Museum of Art, New York) ordered from
Duncan Phyfe for the parlor of New York
lawyer Samuel A. Foot's new home at 678
Broadway (see no. 30). The treatment of
the scrolled supports also relates to those
found on at least two pier tables by Phyfe,
one originally made for his daughter, Eliza
Vail, which bears a label used during the
period 1837–40, and a second, which was
included on an 1834 bill of sale to The
White House, Washington, D.C. All of
these pieces reflect the heavier, more
architectonic style of the French
Restauration. They were undoubtedly
derived from various plates published in
Paris during the years 1825–27 by Pierre
de la Mésangère, which also influenced the
extensive "pillar and scroll" production of
J. & J. W. Meeks in New York, John Hall
in Baltimore, and scores of other cabinetmakers from Boston to New Orleans.

GEORGE HARVEY
(about 1800–1878)

36.
Sunnyside, 1836

Oil on wood panel, 17½ x 23¼ in.
Signed and dated (at lower right):
G. Harvey 1836

EX COLL.: Washington Irving, New York;
to his niece, Charlotte Van Wart Irving,
New York; by descent in the family,
until 1987

The English-born artist and architect
George Harvey began his association with
Washington Irving in the early 1830s when
Harvey settled at Hastings-on-Hudson,
New York. Between 1835 and 1837 Irving
consulted Harvey frequently for designs
and drafts in the remodeling of his house,
"Sunnyside," at Irvington-on-Hudson.
During the Neo-Classical period there was
continuing interest in the Gothic style.
Harvey's design for Sunnyside combines
classical symmetry, Gothic details, and
stepped gables reminiscent of the old
Dutch houses that survived along the
Hudson from New York to Albany and
that were rapidly being replaced by Greek
Revival buildings.

JOHN LUDLOW MORTON
(1792–1871)

37.
Going Out Riding, about 1838

Oil on canvas, 18 x 24 in.

EXHIBITED: Hirschl & Adler Galleries, New York, 1982, *American Art from the Colonial and Federal Periods*, p. 100 no. 88 illus.

EX COLL.: the artist, until 1871; by descent in the artist's family, until 1981; to [Hirschl & Adler Galleries, New York, 1981–83]; to private collection, 1983–91

Until the end of the first quarter of the nineteenth century the production of American artists was heavily weighted towards portraiture. Gradually, landscape, still life, and genre painting also became subjects that found patronage, and by the 1830s American art had become considerably more cosmopolitan in its outlook. Presumably taking the substantial genre of English sporting painting as his model, John Ludlow Morton created a small body of work that, together with the production

of the French emigré Henri Delattre and the Swiss-born Edward Troye, introduced sporting subjects into American art. Either this or a related work titled *Riding in the Countryside* (see: Hirschl & Adler, p. 99 no. 87 illus.) may be the painting shown at the National Academy of Design, New York, 1838, no. 289, as *The Morning Ride, a Scene in the Highlands*.

THOMAS DOUGHTY
(1793–1856)

38.
Landscape: Man Fishing, 1835

Oil on canvas, 21¼ x 28⅛ in.
Signed and dated (at lower center):
T DOUGHTY/1835

Thoughout his mature work, Doughty
paid close attention to local scenery and
the accuracy of detail, while instilling his
landscapes with atmospheric effects that
anticipated the luminist qualities in the
work of the next generation of artists. As
such, his career bridges the topographical
views of the earlier landscape painters in
America and the later sublime landscapes
of the artists of the Hudson River School.

THOMAS COLE
(1801–1848)

39.
Catskill Mountain House, about 1835–40

Oil on canvas, 29 x 36 in.

RECORDED: Earl A. Powell, *Thomas Cole* (1990), p. 103 illus. in color

EXHIBITED: Wadsworth Atheneum, Hartford, Connecticut, and Whitney Museum of American Art, New York, 1948–49, *Thomas Cole, 1801–1848, One Hundred Years Later, A Loan Exhibition*, p. 32 no. 40, lent by Harry Shaw Newman Gallery, New York // Memorial Art Gallery of the University of Rochester, New York; Munson-Williams-Proctor Institute, Utica, New York; Albany Institute of History and Art, New York; and Whitney Museum of American Art, New York, 1969, *Thomas Cole*, pp. 39 no. 51, 100 no. 51 illus., lent by Mr. Calvin and Mrs. C. W. Stillman, New York // Alexander Gallery, New York, 1987, *The Hudson River School: Congenial Observations*, no. 7 illus. in color

EX COLL.: the artist, and by descent to his granddaughter, Mrs. Florence H. Cole Vincent, Catskill, New York; to [Harry Shaw Newman Gallery, New York, 1946–47]; to Mr. Calvin and Mrs. C. W. Stillman, New York

The Catskill Mountain House, seen here in the distance, was built in 1823 in a late-Federal style on a picturesque rocky ledge some 2,250 feet in elevation, near Catskill, New York. A grand hotel, it was a favorite retreat for wealthy Americans seeking refuge in the mountains. Thomas Cole painted the hotel and its surrounding landscape from different locations a number of times, beginning in the late 1820s until about 1847. The largest of these is *A View of the Two Lakes and Mountain House, Catskill Mountains, Morning* of 1844–45 (The Brooklyn Museum, New York), which shares with this work a similar vantage point.

Here, a dark and powerful rain storm hovers above the Mountain House, contrasting with the raging fire at the right from which large plumes of smoke emerge. Such drama is typical of Cole's Romantic and highly expressive landscapes, where the awesome power of nature is glorified, reminding the viewer of man's own insignificance.

WILLIAM R. HAMILTON
(about 1810–about 1865)

40a.
Portrait of Alexander Masterton, about
1834

40b.
Portrait of Euphenus Masterton, about
1834

Each, oil on canvas, 35½ x 28½ in.

EX COLL.: Mr. and Mrs. Alexander
Masterton, Bronxville, New York; to their
daughter, Mary Masterton Dusenberry,
Bronxville; to her daughter, Miss Amie
Sykes Dusenberry, Bronxville; by bequest
to Miss Vivian O. Wills, Bronxville,
1959–85

Originally from Scotland, Alexander Masterton (1797–1859) was an influential architect-builder, who helped to shape the Greek Revival character of much of the architecture in New York during the second quarter of the nineteenth century. Soon after his arrival in 1817 he formed a construction partnership in New York and a few years later became involved with quarrying the newly-discovered Tuckahoe marble in Westchester County, which became an important source of high-grade marble for the numerous classical buildings that were springing up across America. The first major building that

Masterton worked on was the architect Martin E. Thompson's United States Branch Bank, on Wall Street, of 1822–24, which was later reconstructed as the facade of The American Wing at The Metropolitan Museum of Art, New York. Masterton married Euphenus Morison (d. 1860) during the 1820s, and the following decade the family moved to Bronxville.

Masterton was instrumental in arranging for the Scottish-born portrait painter William R. Hamilton to come to the United States, and for promoting his career in New York. Hamilton arrived about 1832, and in 1833 was elected an

Associate Member of the National Academy of Design, New York, where he exhibited until at least 1841. Many of his portraits of the 1830s were of prominent Scottish-born New Yorkers, almost certainly introduced to the artist by Masterton.

Until recent years these two portraits (which are framed together in their original Greek Revival frame) and those of the Mastertons' son (see no. 41) and other members of the family remained in the Greek Revival Masterton house in Bronxville, together with many of the original furnishings.

WILLIAM R. HAMILTON
(about 1810–about 1865)

41.
Portrait of John Morison Masterton, 1838

Oil on canvas, 49½ x 37½ in.
Signed, dated, and inscribed (on the back,
prior to lining): W. R. Hamilton
pinxt./1838

EXHIBITED: National Academy of
Design, New York, 1838, no. 77

EX COLL.: Mr. and Mrs. Alexander
Masterton, Bronxville, New York; to their
daughter, Mary Masterton Dusenberry,
Bronxville; to her daughter, Miss Amie
Sykes Dusenberry, Bronxville; by bequest
to Miss Vivian O. Wills, Bronxville,
1959–85

John M. Masterton was closely associated
with his father, Alexander Masterton (see
no. 40a), in the marble and building
industry in New York. By 1870 John
Masterton was listed as the sole owner of
the lucrative Eastchester Marble Quarry
Company, which his father had formed in
1854. However, John also became involved
in the banking business with "Boss"
Tweed of Tammany Hall, and, after
several years of what appeared to be a
successful operation, suddenly went
bankrupt. In 1884 he was indicted on four
counts of first degree larceny in connection
with a banking swindle.

Young John is depicted here in a
costume typical of the 1830s. The Doric
column, commonly seen in Greek Revival
architecture, is a standard prop of the
period but here may also be a reference to
his father's construction and marble
quarrying businesses.

WILLIAM JAMES BENNETT
(1787–1844)

42.

A Brisk Gale — Bay of New York, 1839

Aquatint, 19¾ x 25⅝ in.
First state of four

REFERENCES: Dale Roylance, *William James Bennett: Master of the Aquatint View* (The New York Public Library, 1988), no. 37 // I. N. Phelps Stokes, *The Iconography of Manahattan Island* (1915–26), III, pp. 619–622

William James Bennett received early training in the disciplines of watercolor and aquatint while a student at the Royal Academy, London. He moved to America around 1826, and by 1832 had embarked on a series of folio engravings now recognized as the finest collection of nineteenth-century American city views ever issued.

Like many of his counterparts at the National Academy of Design, Bennett revelled in the dramatic possibilities found along the Hudson. His *Brisk Gale* is not only an engaging view of a bustling New York Harbor, but a superb marine subject in its own right, the composition is highly charged with the power implicit in the wind, sea, and precariously balanced craft under sail. The row of Greek "temples" on the shoreline in the distance are the buildings of Sailor's Snug Harbor at New Brighton, Staten Island, which still stand today.

A BRISK GALE, BAY OF NEW YORK

ASHER B. DURAND
(1796–1886)

43.
Classical Composition, 1850

Oil on canvas, 33½ x 48½ in.

RECORDED: Henry T. Tuckerman, *Book of the Artists, American Artist Life* (1867), p. 196, as *Classic Italy*

EXHIBITED: Hirschl & Adler Galleries, New York, 1974, *Quality — An Experience in Collecting*, no. 10 illus. // Hirschl & Adler Galleries, New York, 1977, *A Gallery Collects*, no. 19 illus. // Haus der Kunst, Munich, West Germany, 1983, *Im Licht von Claude Lorrain*, pp. 274, 275 illus. // Museum of the Borough of Brooklyn, Brooklyn College, New York, 1986, *Now Reposing in Greenwood Cemetery*, no. 25

EX COLL.: Painted for Mr. John Wolfe; to sale, John Wolfe Collection, H. H. Leeds & Co., New York, Dec. 22–23, 1863, no. 15; Emoray Collection; Richard I. Pearce

Although executed in 1850, this painting is virtually a mirror image of Durand's *Morning of Life*, one of a pair of monumental compositions he executed in 1838 (National Academy of Design, New York). The 1838 works parallel the development of the allegorical paintings done in pairs and series by Hudson River School founder, Thomas Cole. Also referred to in the nineteenth century as *Classic Italy*, *Classical Composition* reveals the influence of seventeenth-century French Romantic landscape painters, most notably Claude Lorrain, in the tranquil scene bathed in golden afternoon light and in the distinctly classicizing architectural and sculptural motifs.

BOSTON

44.

Neo-Classical Convex Mirror, American or English, about 1810–15

Pine, painted and gilded, mirror plate, glass bobeches and prisms, and various metals, 43 in. high

RECORDED: *American Antiques from the Israel Sack Collection*, IX (1989), p. 2531 no. P6156 illus.

ON DEPOSIT: Portland Museum of Art, Maine, 1970–88

EX COLL.: Derby Family, Salem, Massachusetts, and by descent to Sarah Derby, until 1989

A new style of looking glass, the convex, or girandole, mirror, was introduced in America about 1800. This form was advertised by retailers here before it actually appeared in local price books, leading to the conclusion that the earliest examples were probably imported from England. A popular alternative to the rectangular pier glass, these circular convex mirrors incorporated a whole vocabulary of Neo-Classical ornament.

This beautifully carved and perfectly balanced mirror and its mate with an opposing eagle, now in the Portland Museum of Art, Maine, were originally purchased by the family of the wealthy Salem merchant Elias Haskett Derby and descended in the Derby family. The Portland Museum attributes its mirror to John Doggett (1780–1857), the well-known frame and mirror maker of Roxbury, Massachusetts.

Israel Sack, Inc.

67

JESSE CHURCHILL
(1773–1819)
and
DANIEL TREADWELL
(active 1805–1816), Boston

45.
Presentation Urn, about 1816

Silver, 14½ in. high
Marked (on the bottom): Churchill
&/Treadwell
Engraved (on the front): GRAND LODGE
OF MASSACHUSETTS/to/THE
REVEREND and RIGHT WORSHIPFUL
BROTHER/THADDEUS MASON HARRIS.
D. D./PAST GRAND CHAPLAIN and
CORRESPONDING SECRETARY./A. L.
5816 [1816]./MEMORIA tenemus quae non
remunerare possumus.

This sophisticated and elegant covered
presentation piece exemplifies the best of
Boston silver of the late Federal, or early
Empire, period. A parallel to the beautiful
and tasteful furniture of Thomas Seymour's Boston Cabinet Manufactory, it
preserves the delicate scale of the Federal
period, but anticipates Empire taste, not
only in its use of the eagle and bail
handles and the paw feet, but in its
general form as well. Related to a wine
cooler at the Amherst College Art
Museum, Massachusetts, with a dedicatory
inscription to Oliver Hazard Perry, this
urn was made for presentation to a
distinguished Mason, Thaddeus Mason
Harris (1768–1842), the first Grand
Chaplain of the Grand Lodge of
Massachusetts.

Private collection

J. B. BINON
(active in Boston 1818–20)

46.

Bust of Major General Henry Dearborn,
1818

Unfired clay, gessoed and painted, 28 in.
high, on original wooden base, painted
and marbleized, 41 in. high
Signed, dated, and inscribed (on proper
right side): Binon de Lyons/Eleve de
Chinard/Boston 1818

EXHIBITED: Hirschl & Adler Galleries,
New York, 1989, *Uncommon Spirit:
Sculpture in America 1800–1940*, pp. 10–11
no. 3 illus.

EX COLL.: Lorenzo de Medici Sweat,
Portland, Maine; to Mr. Clapp, Portland;
to C. H. Robinson, Portland

J. B. Binon received his early training in
his native Lyons, France, under the
sculptor Joseph Chinard, who specialized
in portrait busts, particularly of the
Bonaparte family and Napoleonic generals,
and allegorical figure groups. Binon
arrived in Boston around 1818, and was
almost certainly the first European-trained
sculptor to have worked there. He created
portrait busts of important Americans,
among them John Adams and this one of
Henry Dearborn, but he is perhaps best
remembered for his early influence on the
important Neo-Classical sculptor Horatio
Greenough (see no. 98).

Henry Dearborn (1751–1829) served
in many distinguished government
positions. He was an officer during the
Revolutionary War, a Congressman from
Massachusetts, the Secretary of War
during Thomas Jefferson's Presidency, the
Collector of the Port of Boston, the Major
General of Militia and United States
Marshall for the District of Maine, and,
finally, from 1822 to 1824, the Minister
to Portugal.

A marble version of this bust, also
dated 1818, is in the Chicago Historical
Society.

47.
Pair of Neo-Classical Side Chairs,
Boston, about 1810–20

Mahogany, 33 in. high

RECORDED: *cf.* The Metropolitan
Museum of Art, New York, *19th Century
America, Furniture and Other Decorative Arts*
(1970), fig. 30

This pair of klismos-form side chairs (one
illustrated) represents a model typical of
the Boston school of chair making during
the years 1810–15. Most probably inspired
by designs for "Grecian" chairs published
in the *London Chair-Makers' and Carvers' Book
of Prices for Workmanship* of 1802 and 1808,
the pair successfully demonstrates several
regional characteristics, such as the boldly
reeded rails and the central tablet
accenting the crest rail, here carved with
anthemia, but occassionally ornamented
with lyres, acanthus leaves, or rosettes.

Israel Sack, Inc.

48.

Lyre-Base Work Table, Boston, about
1815–20

Mahogany, with bird's-eye maple panels,
and with brass paw toe caps and castors,
stringing, string inlay, and knobs,
31 x 24 x 18 in.

The lyre was used as an important
decorative and structural device throughout the Neo-Classical period, but it took
dramatically different forms in the various
design centers. The elongated lyre on this
complex work table relates to others on
Boston furniture of the 1815–20 period,
particularly a group of work tables and
dressing bureaus associated with John and
Thomas Seymour that show the influence
of English Regency forms. Although this
table bears no specific identification as to
its maker, it is generously inscribed with
the names of a succession of early owners.

Israel Sack, Inc.

Romulus Haskins

William Pitt Fessenden

Attributed to EVERETT HOWARD
(active in New England about 1823)

49.
*Profiles of the Class of 1823 — Bowdoin
College*, 1823

Bound collection of 29 hollow-cut
silhouettes measuring 2¼ x 1¼ in., laid
down against black silk backgrounds on
pages measuring 8¼ x 6¼ in.
Most profiles signed by the sitters, the
title page and mounts inscribed in the
owner's hand (classmate Howard H.
Hobbes) identifying the sitters and their
respective hometowns.

There was tremendous interest in the craft
of silhouette, or "shade making," in
America during the first decades of the
nineteenth century, prior to the introduction of the daguerreotype. These
portrait miniatures were popular in large
part because they represented an inex-
pensive and speedy way to produce
accurate likenesses. Their evocation of
ancient Greek black figure vase painting
undoubtedly contributed to their
popularity as well.

The examples in this album, a
prototype of the modern college yearbook,
commemorate members of the graduating
class of 1823 from Bowdoin College. They
are possibly from the hand of Everett

Howard, an itinerant profilist recorded as
having sought commissions from the
collegians of Bowdoin during his travels
about New England in search of work.

Some of the eager young men whose
shadows are captured here, like Romulus
Haskins, were patrician in name, while the
careers of others, such as William Pitt
Fessenden, actually fulfilled that role.
Fessenden (1806–69) served multiple
terms both in the Maine legislature and
the United States Senate, where he gained
renown as one of the most effective
proponents of the anti-slavery cause. He
also served as Secretary of the Treasury
during the Civil War and was an early
regent of the Smithsonian Institution.

ALVAN FISHER
(1792–1863)

50a.
View of Harvard College, 1821

Ink wash heightened with Chinese white
on paper, 9½ x 14½ in.
Signed and dated (at lower left):
A. Fisher 1821

50b.
Scene at Harvard College, 1821

Ink wash on paper, 9⅛ x 14¼ in.
EX COLL.: by descent in the artist's family,
until 1988

Alvan Fisher was born in Needham,
Massachusetts, and was raised in neigh-
boring Dedham. He began his career in
1812 as a portrait painter, but turned to
landscape as early as 1815. As one of the
country's first landscape painters, Fisher
provided a foundation for the American
landscape tradition, which reached its full
flowering with the artists of the Hudson
River School. Unlike the romantic,
idealized landscapes of such artists as
Thomas Cole (see nos. 26 and 39),
however, Fisher's work displays an interest
in topography and specific views based in
the English topographic tradition.
    Fisher made this pair of drawings in
conjunction with a commission from
Cummings & Hilliard of Boston to
execute two views of Harvard College for
reproduction as engravings. These drawings depict the early Harvard buildings as seen from Cambridge Common,
with Christ Church, Cambridge, seen at
the far right in *View of Harvard College.*

51.

Pier Table, Boston, about 1820–25

Rosewood, with ormolu mounts, gilt brass on lead moldings, mirror plate, and marble top, 35½ x 47⅝ x 20½ in. (including marble top)

In the taste of the French Restauration, this elaborate and sophisticated table (one of a near pair, the other, Hirschl & Adler Galleries) exhibits many characteristics that specifically define a Boston style of about 1820–25, including flattened ebonized bun feet surrounded by ormolu bands and ormolu moldings outlining various recessed panels, some of which display superbly cast and chiseled ormolu mounts that were most likely imported from France. Although unmarked, it is close in style and detailing to pieces labelled by the Boston firms of Isaac Vose and Sons, and Emmons and Archibald, who are known to have produced furniture of this quality and style in Boston during the early years of the nineteenth century.

52.
Neo-Classical Sofa,
Boston, about 1825

Mahogany, 35⅛ x 87⅝ x 24⅛ in.

This handsome sofa reflects the influence of the English Regency style, through various fashionable and popular design books of the period, on a group of cabinetmakers working in Boston about 1825. The highly figured mahogany veneers, bold forms incorporating sweeping curves, and robustly carved stylized Classical Revival ornament, often featuring anthemia, tulips, and scrolls (see no. 53), typify the aesthetic and stylistic preferences of a number of Boston cabi-

netmakers of this period. Just as Duncan Phyfe is credited with the work of a whole school of cabinetmakers in New York, so a Boston style is usually associated with the names of Emmons and Archibald, Isaac Vose and Sons, and a number of other artisans whose names are known from labels or stencils on a few pieces of Boston furniture of this period. The Boston directories suggest, however, that a substantial number of cabinetmakers were responsible for the quantity of beautiful furniture produced in Boston during this period.

WILLIAM FISK
(active about 1810–1835), Boston

53.
Sewing Table with Drop Leaves, about 1820–30

Mahogany, with brass castors and escutcheons, 29⅝ x 20 x 19¹⁵⁄₁₆ in. (19¹⁵⁄₁₆ x 37¼ with both leaves extended) Stenciled (in second drawer): WM. FISK/Cabinet Maker/Washington St./BOSTON

This handsome table, made by William Fisk of Boston, defines a Boston style (see no. 52) of the 1820s. Fisk worked at various Washington Street locations from before 1810 until after 1835. As a model for his design, Fisk may have referred to George Smith's *Cabinet-Maker's and Upholsterer's Guide* (London: 1826) which shows a "Backgammon Work Table" (pl. 8) of similar composition.

WILLIAM CARLETON
(active about 1820–1860), Boston

54.
Pair of Small Sinumbra Lamps,
about 1825

Bronze, patinated and gilt, with frosted
and cut glass shades, 16½ in. high
Marked (on embossed brass labels attached
to each): MANUFACTURED BY/W.
CARLETON/BOSTON

Although much of the lighting used in the
United States during the Neo-Classical
period was imported from England and
France, certain businesses here did
produce a variety of lighting devices. Some
firms, amomg them the New England
Glass Company of Cambridge,
Massachusetts (see no. 55), and the
Boston and Sandwich Glass Company,
Sandwich, Massachusetts, made a vast
array of lighting devices, including some
that were quite simple in form; other
firms, however, made lamps that were in
the latest and most fashionable English or
French taste. This diminutive pair of
sinumbra lamps, totally original
throughout, bear the same embossed labels
as found on numerous lamps made in
England (see no. 93), but the text "MANU-
FACTURED BY/W. CARLETON/BOSTON"
is clearly meant to distinguish them from
similar imports. According to the Boston
directories, Carleton was active at various
Boston addresses as "tinman," "manufacturer," and "lamp manufacturer" from
1820 on.

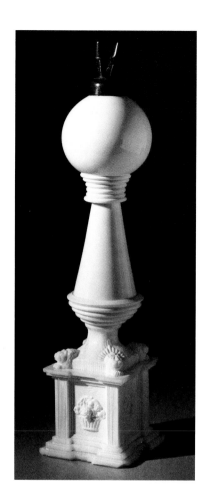

Attributed to ENOCH ROBINSON
and SPENCER RICHARDS, NEW
ENGLAND GLASS COMPANY,
Cambridge, Massachusetts
or
BOSTON AND SANDWICH
GLASS COMPANY, Sandwich,
Massachusetts

55.
*Opaque White Fluid Lamp with Lion
Heads and Baskets of Flowers,* about
1828–35

Glass, pressed and blown, with pewter
burner, 15⅛ in. high (to top of burner)
EX COLL.: [James H. Rose, Canton, Ohio,
1967]; to William J. Elsholz, Detroit,
1967–86

Among the most elaborate lamps produced
in New England during the Classical
Revival period were the so-called "lion-
head" lamps, which incorporate couchant
lions and baskets of flowers against a
formal background of fluted pilasters.
Some of these lamps bear both the name
of the New England Glass Company and
the initials E.R — S.R., which are said to
stand for Enoch Robinson and Spencer
Richards, the former of whom took out
one of the earliest patents for glass
pressing in the United States. This lamp,
of unusually large scale, is nearly identical
to a pair in The Metropolitan Museum of
Art, New York.

BASS OTIS
(1784–1861)

57a.
Portrait of Mr. David Sears, Jr., 1830

Oil on canvas, 36 x 28½ in.
Signed, dated, and inscribed (at lower
right): B. Otis Pinxt Decr. 1830

57b.
Portrait of Mrs. David Sears, Jr., 1830

Oil on canvas, 36 x 28½ in.

EX COLL.: Robert Fulton Sears, and his
estate, until 1986; to sale, Samuel T.
Freeman & Co., Philadelphia, Nov. 4,
1986, no. 398

David Sears, Jr. (1787–1871) and Miriam
Clark Mason (1790–1870) were married in
1809. At various times between 1816 and
1851 David Sears served in the Massachusetts Legislature, first as a representative

and later as a state senator. He is further distinguished for building Sears Tower, an astronomical observatory, at Harvard University.

As a member of the nation's growing patron class of wealthy men, Sears commissioned work from some of the most prominent artists, architects, and craftsmen of the day, including the architect Alexander Parris, who designed the Sears home on Beacon Street (now the Somerset Club), an unidentified cabinetmaker who executed a refined *secrétaire à abattant* now in The Art Institute of Chicago, and the distinguished Philadelphia silversmith Anthony Rasch, who made an elaborate suite of table silver for the Sears' new townhouse (see no. 72).

These portraits, which retain their original Greek Revival frames, portray Mr. and Mrs. Sears seated in Neo-Classical chairs. Both are stylishly attired, he in a trimmed waistcoat, she in a dress with leg-of-mutton sleeves that were then in fashion.

Worcester Rail Road.   Painted & Engraved by Rob.t Havell.   Bunkers Hill   Lowell Rail Road.

Coloured by Havell & Son.nr   Printed by R. Havell.

VIEW OF THE CITY OF BOSTON

FROM DORCHESTER HEIGHTS.

Published by W.A. Coleman 205 Broadway for Rob.t Havell Sing Sing N.York.

Entered according to Act of Congress in the year 1841 by Rob.t Havell in the District Clerks office of the United States for the Southern District of N.York.

ROBERT HAVELL, JR.
(1793–1878)

58.
*View of the City of Boston from
Dorchester Heights*, 1841

Color aquatint with touches of hand-
coloring, 12½ x 17⅝ in.
First and only state

RECORDED: *cf.* Gloria Gilda Deak,
Picturing America 1497–1899 (1988),
no. 509

Robert Havell came to America from his
native England in 1839, having established
his reputation as the engraver of John
James Audubon's *The Birds of America* (see
nos. 97a and 97b). Like his contemporary
William James Bennett (see no. 42), he
was both a master printmaker and an
accomplished watercolorist in the British
landscape tradition. Havell and a handful
of his transplanted countrymen were
among the few people in America at the
time capable of realizing their artistic
vision in aquatint, a demanding medium
unmatched for its ability to replicate the
delicate effects of watercolor.

A sense of well-being and serenity
pervades the artist's sweeping depiction of
Boston, one of seven city views he
executed shortly after his arrival in this
country. Across a tranquil harbor, grand
and lofty public structures dominate
the skyline, much as they would have in
the city-states of antiquity, lending a
distinctively idyllic character to the scene.

Attributed to BOSTON AND
SANDWICH GLASS COMPANY,
Sandwich, Massachusetts
or
NEW ENGLAND GLASS
COMPANY, Cambridge, Massachusetts

59a.
Strawberry Diamond Bowl with Cross,
before 1830

Glass, pressed, 1¼ x 12 (diam.) in.

Attributed to BOSTON AND
SANDWICH GLASS COMPANY,
Sandwich, Massachusetts

59b.
Blown Three-Mold Footed Punchbowl,
about 1825–35

Glass, blown-molded, 5¼ x 8 (diam.) in.

During the 1820s various American glass houses produced different wares that attempted to replicate the fine cut glass being produced by English, Irish, and Continental factories. Improvements made to the manufacture of pressed glass, often credited to Deming Jarves who worked at the Boston and Sandwich Glass Company, in about 1827, expanded the American repertory of forms and designs and played a profound role in the development of glassmaking both here and abroad.

The rare clear strawberry diamond bowl with cross, one of two known examples in this large size, uses the pressing machine to achieve the effect of glass sharply cut in the so-called "strawberry diamond" design. And the clear blown three-mold footed punchbowl, in which the pattern is achieved by blowing glass into a patterned mold, uses a different technique to suggest the richness of fine imported cut glass.

Attributed to BOSTON AND
SANDWICH GLASS COMPANY,
Sandwich, Massachusetts

60a.
Bowl, about 1835

Glass, pressed, 2⅛ x 11 (diam.) in.

60b.
Tripod Candlestick, about 1835

Glass, pressed, 6¹³⁄₁₆ in. high

60c.
Covered Honey Dish, about 1835

Glass, pressed, 8⅛ x 6 in. (overall)

Although the earliest pressed glass made in
America attempted to imitate expensive
cut glass from abroad, after 1835 or so
various New England factories produced
pressed glass with a stippled, or "lacy,"
background, which was meant to give glass
that was oftentimes impure in content an
added brilliance. Collectively, the works
shown here illustrate a whole repertory of
Neo-Classical designs. A rare covered
honey dish, itself in the form of a lyre,
incorporates shields, diamonds, and fans,
as well as the so-called "Peacock Eye," said
to have been inspired by the appearance of
Haley's Comet in 1835. The unusual
tripod candlestick uses paw feet and
scrolls in much the same way they appear
in furniture and silver designs of the
period. And the extraordinary eleven-inch
bowl adds acanthus leaves, rope borders,
and tulips to other familiar motifs of the
time to create a classic of pressed glass of
the Empire period. Although it is
tempting to suggest that these designs
derive from "lacy" glass being produced at
various French and Belgian glass houses,
the direction of influence remains
uncertain. Europeans also held a
fascination for American technology,
prompting European museums to collect
examples of glass from various New
England factories for the instruction of
local craftsmen.

PHILADELPHIA, BALTIMORE, AND WASHINGTON, D.C.

REMBRANDT PEALE
(1778–1860)

61.
Portrait of Three Children, about 1809

Oil on canvas, 27 x 24 in.

RECORDED: Letter, Carol Eaton Hevner, University of Pennsylvania, Philadelphia, to the former owner of the painting, March 6, 1987 (Hirschl & Adler archives)

EX COLL.: Mrs. Virginia Heulings Smith Brinkerhoff; by descent to private collection, Maryland, until 1988

Following in the tradition established by his father, Charles Willson Peale, and other artists of the preceding generation, Rembrandt Peale concentrated primarily on portraiture for his livelihood. Through Gilbert Stuart, who arrived in Philadelphia in 1795, Rembrandt was exposed early on to the more naturalistic, painterly style of the English School of portraiture, which characterized his early work. During trips to Paris in 1808 and 1809–10, however, the artist was able to study the more restrained Neo-Classical style of such French painters as David, Gérard, and Girodet, and their influence radically affected his work from that point on.

Carol E. Hevner, who is currently preparing the catalogue raisonné of the work of Rembrandt Peale, has noted that although the present work relates stylistically to Rembrandt's early portraits, the "dewier flesh" of the three sitters "suggests a post-Paris portrait such as that of *Edward Shippen Bird* (National Museum of American Art, Washington, D.C.)." Hevner wrote: "Its more sophisticated composition, which easily accommodates three figures, suggests the experience of the kind of accomplished works he was able to study in Paris." She continued, "In this case ... I believe we have an example of Peale striking a balance between his Anglo-American style and his more classicizing French style."

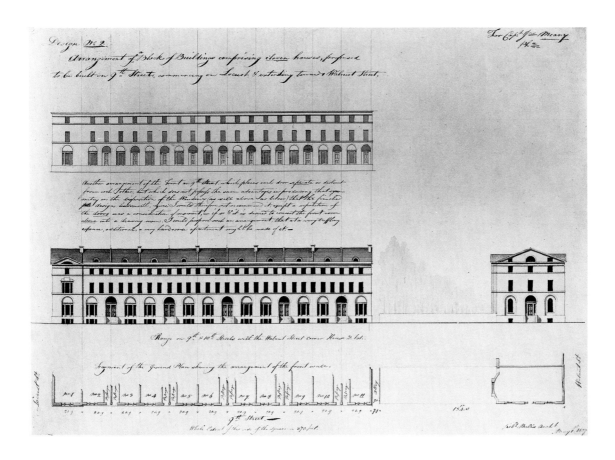

ROBERT MILLS
(1781–1855)

62.
Franklin Row: Design No. 2, 1809

Pen and ink and watercolor on paper,
14¼ x 20⁹⁄₁₆ in.
Signed, dated, and inscribed (at lower right): Robt Mills Archt/May 1st 1809; (at upper right): For Capt Jno Meany/Pha.; (at upper left): Design No 2/Arrangement of a Block of Buildings comprising eleven houses, proposed to be built on 9th Street, commencing on Locust, & extending towards Walnut Street.; (at center): Another arrangement of the Front on 9th Street, which places each door separate or distinct/from each other, but which does not possess the same advantages, in producing that sym-/metry in the disposition of the Windows . . .

RECORDED: John M. Bryan, ed., *Robert Mills Architect* (1989), pp. 29, 41–42, illus. p. 42 fig. 2.6

EX COLL.: [Charles Sessler, Philadelphia, until 1967]; to the Dietrich American Foundation, Philadelphia, until 1985

Mills, a native of Charleston, South Carolina, was, according to Roger G. Kennedy [*Greek Revival America* (1989), p. 22], "the first of two American-born architects to work confidently in the Greek style, the other being William Strickland."

In the 1830s Mills served as superintendent of public buildings in Washington, D.C., replacing his former teacher, Benjamin Henry Latrobe. Mills took over the design and construction of Franklin Row (1809–10), Philadelphia, after Latrobe became frustrated with his client, Captain John Meany. Mills' design for Franklin Row is typical of the row houses that would soon ornament whole areas of Philadelphia, New York, and Boston, and serve as the background for the Neo-Classical paintings and furnishings that a growing band of artists and artisans was producing.

Private collection

RAPHAELLE PEALE
(1774–1825)

63a.
Still Life of Fruit, Pitcher, and Pretzel,
1810

Oil on wood panel, 11¼ x 13 in.
Inscribed (by another hand, on the back):
Son of/Charles Willson Peale; (on old
label): Painted by Raphael [sic] Peale/Year
1810/Son of Charles Willson Peale;
inscribed (on the back, upper right
corner): Raphael [sic] Peale/Year 1810

63b.
Table Top Still Life with Jug and Fish,
1810

Oil on canvas, 12 x 13 in.
Signed (at lower right): Rape: Peale Pxt;
inscribed (by another hand, on back label):
Painted by/Raphael [sic] Peale/Son
of/Charles Willson Peale/Year 1810

EXHIBITED: Hirschl & Adler Galleries,
New York, 1988–89, *Variations on a Theme:
Still Life Painting in America,* nos. 43 and 44

EX COLL.: the artist; to his second son,
Edmund Peale; to his daughter, Louisa
Peale Grimmer; to her son, Charles Alfred
Grimmer, Chattanooga, Tennessee; to his
cousin, Grace Peale Martin, Santa Monica,
California; to her niece, Adah Peale
Stombaugh, until 1987

Unlike his uncle, James Peale, who began
to concentrate on still life painting toward
the end of his career (see no. 75),
Raphaelle Peale devoted himself almost
exclusively to the subject from the start,
and is considered to be the founder of the
still life tradition in America. This pair of
still lifes, datable to 1810 on the basis of
period inscriptions, are among his earliest
works in this genre.

Attributed to JOSEPH B. BARRY &
SON
(active 1810–1822), Philadelphia

64.
Pair of Knife Boxes, about 1810–14

Mahogany, with gilt brass lion-head pulls,
18 x 13½ x 12¾ in.

Knife boxes have always been considered a
rare form in America; until the late
eighteenth century they were mostly
imported from England. This pair (one
illustrated), produced en suite with a
sideboard (illustrated below, not in
exhibition), was originally owned by a
member of the prominent Gratz family of
Philadelphia. The set would seem to
match the description of a "large recess
Sideboard, Barry's make, with column and
side closets [and] a set of knife cases"
offered by the auctioneer John Dorsey in
the May 13, 1814, issue of Poulson's
American Daily Advertiser.

The three pieces relate directly to a
sideboard of essentially similar form,
signed and dated "J. B. Barry 1813" (see:
Robert T. Trump, "Joseph B. Barry,
Philadelphia Cabinetmaker," in *The
Magazine Antiques*, CXXII [May 1989],
p. 1214 pl. III illus.). All were most likely
inspired by a design for a sideboard
published as plate 92 in George Smith's
*Collection for Household Furniture and Interior
Decoration* (London: 1808).

The knife boxes and matching
sideboard incorporate many of the
signature details of the Barry workshop,
including tapered reeded columns with
acanthus leaf capitals and hairy-paw feet,
features which also appear on various
chests of drawers, chairs, and a pier table
attributed to Barry. Other significant
details include the use of richly figured
mahogany veneers and the pointed, or
Gothic arch, panels on the doorfronts on
both the sideboard and knife boxes.

The Henry Francis du Pont Winterthur
Museum

HARVEY LEWIS
(active 1813–1825), Philadelphia

65.
Handled Cake Basket, 1815

Silver, 11½ x 12⅛ x 9½ in.
Marked (twice, on the bottom): HARVEY
LEWIS
Inscribed (on the bottom): Presented by
Anthony Stocker/to Patty R. Stocker
/Feb.y 15. 1815.

EX COLL.: Anthony Stocker; by gift to
Patty R. Stocker, in 1815

Philadelphia was the undisputed center of
silversmithing in America during the Neo-
Classical period, and Harvey Lewis was
one of its most distinguished practitioners.
This refined basket, ornamented by die-
rolled borders, cast paw feet, repoussé
grape vines and cornucopia, and engraved
leaves and a crest on the handle, speaks
loudly of a local Philadelphia style of
silver, just as the Haines-Connely School
and Quervelle and his followers define
successive phases of Philadelphia furniture
design.

Private collection

WILLIAM RUSH
(1756–1833)

66.
Eagle, 1811

Carved wood, gessoed and gilded,
36 x 68 x 61 in.

RECORDED: Philip M. Isaacson, *The American Eagle* (1975), p. 95 fig. 96 // Hirschl & Adler Galleries, New York, *The State of the Arts* (1990), p. 64 fig. 6.1 in color, illus. in color on back cover

EXHIBITED: Assembly Room, Independence Hall, Philadelphia, 1847–1914 // Pennsylvania Museum of Art, Philadelphia, 1937, *William Rush 1756–1833: The First Native American Sculptor*, pp. 30–31 no. 9 // Pennsylvania Academy of the Fine Arts, Philadelphia, 1982, *William Rush: American Sculptor*, pp. 118, 123 no. 43 illus., 179, 205 no. 14 // Hirschl & Adler Galleries, New York, 1986, *From the Studio: Selections of American Sculpture 1811–1941*, pp. 8–9 no. 1 illus. in color // Hirschl & Adler Galleries, New York, 1989, *Uncommon Spirit: Sculpture in America 1800–1940*, pp. 3, 6–7 no. 1 illus. in color, illus. in color on back cover

ON DEPOSIT: Historical Society of Pennsylvania, Philadelphia, 1983–86

EX COLL.: St. John's Evangelical Lutheran Church, Philadelphia, 1811–47; by gift to the City of Philadelphia, 1847–1914; returned to St. John's Church, 1914–86

The art of sculpture developed less rapidly than painting in America. Due in large part to the fact that there were few imported models available and almost no opportunity to study the art at home, it was not until the Neo-Classical era that sculpture emerged as a serious art form in the United States. William Rush, considered the "father of American sculpture," was the first important sculptor to come out of the folk art tradition of figurehead and shop sign carving.

In this fully-documented *Eagle* of 1811, Rush created a powerful and realistic symbol that is devoid of the Romantic overtones found in the Neo-Classical marbles of the succeeding generation or in the paintings of his contemporaries. Commissioned by St. John's Evangelical Church in Philadelphia as an emblem of its patron saint, the *Eagle* was installed high above the church's pulpit and held a chain in its mouth that appeared to support the pulpit's sounding board.

FLETCHER & GARDINER
(active 1813–1825), Philadelphia

67.
Ewer with Eagle Handle, about 1815–20

Silver, 11 in. high
Marked (on the bottom): F & G
Engraved (on side, left of spout): DSC

EX COLL.: David and Sarah Cranford,
Prince George's County, Maryland; Henry
family, Maryland, until 1989

The most beautiful silver of the Classical
Revival period in America was made by
Fletcher & Gardiner and Thomas Fletcher,
whose work in Philadelphia collectively
spanned the years 1811–42.

The chaste design of this pyriform
ewer is relieved by the die-rolled borders
of Neo-Classical design, a boldly sculp-
tured eagle's head forming the focal point
of the handle, and elaborately engraved
initials of its first owners, David and Sarah
Cranford.

After JOHN MELISH
(1771–1822)

68a.
Northern Section of the United States including Canada &c., 1816

Engraving with outline color,
14⅞ x 20½ in.

68b.
Southern Section of the United States including Florida &c., 1816

Engraving with outline color,
15⅛ x 19¼ in.

As issued in Klinckowstrom, *Bref om de Forenta Staterne*, Stockholm, 1824.

RECORDED: *cf.* I. N. Phelps Stokes, *The Iconography of Manhattan Island* (1915–26), III, pp. 563–64, pl. 85 // *cf.* Gloria Gilda Deak, *Picturing America 1497–1899* (1988), no. 310

Bound among the aquatint views in the Klinckowstrom travel account, *Letters from the United States,* of 1824 (see no. 17), was a handsome two-part map of the Eastern United States based on John Melish's landmark wall map of 1816, *A Map of the United States with the Contiguous British & Spanish Possessions.* A native of Scotland, Melish was the first publisher in America to make a specialty of geographical works. As one of the outstanding American cartographers of his day, he was an obvious choice for Klinckowstrom as the source for an accurate map of the United States at a time when state and territorial boundaries were undergoing constant revision. As Melish's map reveals, the partitioning of the Trans-Mississippi West had yet to occur at the time of Klinckowstrom's visit, in stark contrast to the accelerated development underway along the Atlantic seaboard.

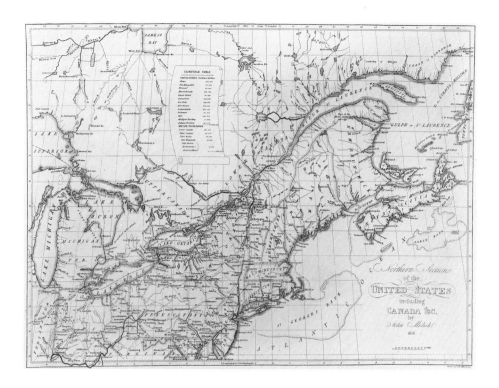

THOMAS SULLY
(1783–1872)

69.
Portrait of Colonel Samuel Boyer Davis,
1819

Oil on canvas, 86 x 60 in.
Signed and dated (at lower right): TS.1819.

RECORDED: Charles Henry Hart, *A Register of Portraits Painted by Thomas Sully 1801–1871* (1909), no. 419, and in addenda // Edward Biddle and Mantle Fielding, *The Life and Works of Thomas Sully* (1921), p. 136 no. 444

EXHIBITED: Pennsylvania Academy of the Fine Arts, Philadelphia, 1820, *Ninth Annual Exhibition of the Pennsylvania Academy of the Fine Arts,* p. 3 no. 4 // The Wilmington Society of the Fine Arts, Delaware, 1958, *Portraits in Delaware 1700–1850,* no. 47 // National Portrait Gallery, Washington, D.C., 1983, *Mr. Sully, Portrait Painter,* pp. 30 no. 31 illus. in color, 74 no. 31 illus.

EX COLL.: Colonel Samuel Boyer Davis; by descent to Sussex Delaware Davis, grandson of the sitter, Philadelphia; to [David David, Inc., Philadelphia, until 1976]; to [Hirschl and Adler Galleries, New York, until 1986]; to private collection, New York

Thomas Sully was perhaps the most "classical" of all of the numerous portrait painters who worked in the United States during the Neo-Classical period. His works show a thorough knowledge of both French and English painting of the period, and epitomize the Romantic mode in American art.

Colonel Davis (1766–1854) was born in Lewes, Sussex County, Delaware. After marrying the daughter of a French nobleman, he served for a short time in the French army, but returned to the United States about 1796. He settled in New Orleans, where he served as Collector of the Port and made a considerable fortune as a planter.

Davis served in the War of 1812, leading the defense of Lewistown, Delaware, and Sandy Hook, New Jersey, against the British, and saw action in the Battle of New Orleans. He was honorably discharged from the army in 1815 and served in the Pennsylvania Legislature from 1831 to 1833.

This dramatic portrait, extremely rare as a heroic full-length, includes a battle scene in the background that may depict Davis' action at Sandy Hook or Lewistown. The portrait was painted for the State of Delaware, which appears never to have taken possession of it. Sully's portrayal of the dashing Colonel reflects the nationalism and spirited individualism that characterized this period in the nation's history.

Private collection

70.

Card Table with Lyre Base, Philadelphia, about 1815

Mahogany, striped maple, and ebonized woods, with ormolu mounts, brass inlay and paw toe caps and castors, and ivory buttons, 29¼ x 35 x 17½ in. (open: 35 x 35 in.)

The lyre, with its association to Greek and Roman antiquity, was one of the most popular motifs of the Neo-Classical period and was often incorporated into the furniture and other decorative arts (see nos. 8 and 48) of the early nineteenth century.

    This table is from a group of card tables by an unidentified Philadelphia cabinetmaker. The design of all of the tables is centered on a pair of open lyres used as supports, but varies in the shape of the skirt (rounded, as here, or stepped), the pattern and arrangement of the ormolu mounts (probably English rather than French in origin), the design of the cast brass feet (paw shaped, as here, or couchant lions), and the quantity and arrangement of various exotic woods and inlays. The circular brass inlays on the ebonized panels at the ends of the skirt appear to be unique to this example.

    Tables of this design are the subject of a comprehensive article by Henry Hawley, "Philadelphia Tables with Lyre Supports," in *The Bulletin of the Cleveland Museum of Art*, LXXV (Jan. 1988), pp. 3–27. A sofa table and various sewing tables of related design can also be assigned to the same shop.

Attributed to JOSEPH B. BARRY &
SON
(active 1810–1822), Philadelphia

71.
*"Eliptic Bureau" with "Columns and
Egyptian Figures",* 1815

Mahogany, with gilded brass knobs,
42 x 47¾ x 23½ in.

RECORDED: *cf.* Robert T. Trump, "Joseph
B. Barry, Philadelphia Cabinetmaker," in
The Magazine Antiques, CXXXII (May 1989),
pp. 1216 pl. V an example with beehive
feet, 1217 pl. VI another example with a
plinth base

This bureau is among the most fully
developed of several examples of a form
that is attributed to Joseph Barry on the
basis of his offer in the *Philadelphia Aurora
General Advertiser* of March 30, 1815, to sell
"3 pair Eliptic Bureaus, columns and
Egyptian figures."

All examples of this type of bureau
have bow fronts with richly figured
mahogany veneers. They stand either on
horizontally reeded legs, usually described
as beehive in shape, or on a plinth base
similar to designs published in George
Smith's *Collection of Designs for Household
Furniture and Interior Decoration* (London:
1808). The tapered square columns with
stylized human feet and busts of
turbanned or unturbanned "Egyptian"
figures are most likely derived from
Thomas Sheraton's *Cabinet Maker,
Upholsterer and General Artist's Encyclopedia*
(London: 1793).

ANTHONY RASCH & COMPANY
(active 1807–1809, 1813–1819, and 1820),
Philadelphia

72.
Pair of Covered Sauce Tureens, about 1820

Silver, 9¼ in. high
Marked (on the bottom of each): A.
RASCH & CO./PHILADELPHIA
Engraved (on the cover of each): D.M.S.
[and crest]

Boston businessman, Harvard overseer,
land developer, and philanthropist David
Sears (1787–1871) and his wife Miriam
Clark Mason Sears (1790–1870) (see
nos. 57a and 57b) built one of the
grandest Classical Revival townhouses in
Boston, designed by the architect Alexander Parris. Forty-two Beacon Street was
erected about 1819–22 and contained
interiors of ultimate sophistication and
workmanship. Among the furnishings that

Mr. and Mrs. Sears ordered was this pair
of sauce tureens (from a set of four) and a
companion soup tureen, which are distinguished by crisply cast leafy knobs,
bearded heads under the handles, paw feet,
and carefully executed repoussé borders,
which cumulatively reflect the best of
English Regency design. The fact that
Sears ordered them from one of the most
distinguished silversmiths in Philadelphia
is perhaps less a testimony to Sears' broad-
ranging business interests than to the fact
that with the disappearance of the firm of
Churchill & Treadwell (see no. 45) about
1816, there was no one in Boston capable
of producing silver of this quality.

Private collection

THOMAS SULLY
(1783–1872)

73.
The Marquis de Lafayette, 1824–25

Pen and ink and wash on paper,
7½ x 4⁵⁄₁₆ in. (sight size)

EXHIBITED: National Portrait Gallery, Washington, D.C., 1983, *Mr. Sully, Portrait Painter*, p. 78 illus. no. 36, as ink and watercolor on paper, 1824 or 1825 // The Queens Museum, New York, 1989, *Lafayette, Hero of Two Worlds*, pp. 150, 152 fig. 141, 154, as 1825

EX COLL.: the artist; to his daughter Jane Sully Darley (Mrs. William Henry Westray Darley); to W. H. W. Darley's friend, Thomas Nash, about 1915 (died about 1926); to his nephew, Mr. Lyman Rhodes, Sharon, Connecticut; to his daughter, Mrs. Elizabeth Rhodes Reynolds, Sharon, Connecticut, until 1977

This is a preparatory drawing for Sully's dramatic full-length portrait of Lafayette in the Independence National Historical Park Collection, Philadelphia. Sully executed this drawing from life in Washington, D.C., during Lafayette's triumphal tour of America in 1824–25. As stated in the National Portrait Gallery catalogue (p. 79), "the drawing would have been completed before Sully had resolved the details of composition for the full-length portrait." In this composition, the hero of the American Revolution is depicted next to a statue based on a Greek or Roman model. He is standing beneath a Neo-Classical triumphal arch, with a scene of his welcoming parade in Philadelphia in the background.

Private collection

RAPHAELLE PEALE
(1774–1825)

74.
Peaches, about 1817

Oil on wood panel, 13⅛ x 19¼ in.

RECORDED: *Milwaukee Journal* (Jan. 11, 1959), illus. in color // *Time* (Mar. 9, 1959), p. 67 illus. in color // Richard York Gallery, New York, *An American Gallery: Volume IV* (1988), no. 1 illus. in color

EXHIBITED: Milwaukee Art Center, Wisconsin, and M. Knoedler & Co., New York, 1959, *Raphaelle Peale (1774–1825): Still Lifes and Portraits*, no. 13 // National Gallery of Art, Washington, D.C., and Pennsylvania Academy of the Fine Arts, Philadelphia, 1988–89, *Raphaelle Peale Still Lifes*, pp. 113 fig. 75 illus. in color, 131 no. 75

EX COLL.: the artist; to his descendants, Langford, Pennsylvania, until about 1948; to private collection, New York

Raphaelle Peale's still lifes are classically composed in the tradition of the seventeenth-century Dutch and Flemish still lifes that he probably would have seen in 1811 and 1815 in exhibitions at the Pennsylvania Academy of the Fine Arts. Here, the delicate balance created between the fruit, the leafy branch, the peeled skin, and the knife belies the apparent randomness of the composition.

JAMES PEALE
(1749–1831)

75.
Still Life with Pears and Grapes,
about 1827

Oil on canvas, 19⅝ x 26½ in.

RECORDED: Letter, Linda C. Simmons,
Associate Curator of Collections, The
Corcoran Gallery of Art, Washington,
D.C., to Meredith Ward, Hirschl & Adler
Galleries, New York, Jan. 27, 1987
(Hirschl & Adler archives)

EX COLL.: [Hirschl & Adler Galleries,
New York, 1986–89]; to private collection

Along with his nephew, Raphaelle Peale
(see nos. 63a, 63b, and 74), James Peale
was one of the two best still-life painters
of the Classical Revival. In an age when
portrait painting was the staple of American art, James created a body of still lifes
that stand at the beginning of a long
tradition in the United States. He
frequently repeated compositions, this
picture duplicating one dated 1827 in the
Pennsylvania Academy of the Fine Arts,
Philadelphia, and another in a private
collection.

Private collection

THOMAS DOUGHTY
(1793–1856)

76.
View of the Fairmount Waterworks,
Philadelphia, from the Opposite Side of the
Schuylkill River, about 1824–26

Oil on canvas, 21¼ x 29 in.

Signed (at lower right): Thomas Doughty

EXHIBITED: Philadelphia Museum of Art,
1988, *The Fairmount Waterworks, 1812–1911*
(checklist in *Bulletin,* 84, Summer 1988),
p. 41

EX COLL.: Eli Kirk Price (1797–1884),
Philadelphia, until 1884; to the estate of
Eli Kirk Price, in 1884; and by descent,
until 1987; to [Hirschl & Adler Galleries,
New York, 1987–88]; to private collection,
1988–91

A native of Philadelphia, Thomas
Doughty was, along with Alvan Fisher
(see nos. 50a and 50b), Thomas Cole (see
nos. 26 and 39), and Thomas Birch (see
no. 87), one of the earliest professional
landscape painters in America. This *View
of the Fairmount Waterworks* is an important
example of his early, more topographical
style.

Celebrated for its charming gardens,
dams, reservoirs, turning waterwheels, and
classically-inspired buildings, the Fairmount Waterworks was a favorite spot
among Philadelphians for strolling and
admiring the scenery along the Schuylkill
River. Its popularity is dramatically
illustrated by the vast number of people
shown in Doughty's painting. The facility,

including the buildings, the machinery,
the distribution system, and the surrounding gardens, was largely designed by the
engineer Frederick C. Graff (1774–1847)
and constructed over a period of about
forty years, beginning in 1812. As a young
man Graff had assisted the architect and
engineer Benjamin Henry Latrobe (1764–
1820) and later served as superintendant of
the first Philadelphia Waterworks at
Centre Square, designed by Latrobe. The
influence of Latrobe's Neo-Classical
architectural style is evident in Graff's
designs, where the machinery of the
waterworks was housed in structures based
on Greek prototypes that were attractive
and harmonious additions to their
surroundings.

After THOMAS DOUGHTY
(1793–1856)

Engraved by CEPHAS CHILDS
(1793–1871)

77.
*To Joseph S. Lewis, This View of Fair
Mount Works, is inscribed by a number of
his fellow citizens as a tribute of respect
and gratitude for the eminent service he has
rendered the City of Philadelphia...,* about
1826

Etching and engraving, 17½ x 21¼ in.

RECORDED: cf. Gloria Gilda Deák,
Picturing America 1497–1899 (1988),
no. 333

Beginning in 1824 the celebrated
Philadelphia engraver Cephas Childs
transferred to copperplate a number of
views of the waterworks after paintings by
Thomas Doughty, of which this is the
finest.

A review of the literature recording
Doughty's different versions of the subject
suggests that the exact canvas which
provided the prototype for Childs' design
has yet to be found.

An alternative theory is that Childs
merely used one of the Doughty paintings
as the point of departure for his own
accomplished engraving, which places
greater emphasis on the buildings and less
on the poetic character of the landscape

framing the site. The engraver's straight-forward treatment of the subject is entirely in keeping both with the requirements of a commercially successful topographical view and the print's dedication to Joseph S. Lewis, one of the chief financial backers of the Waterworks.

Childs betrays his affection for the Waterworks in his *Views of Philadelphia,* 1827–30: "The situation of Fairmount is exceedingly picturesque, and the works themselves are constructed with great neatness. It is a favorite resort of the citizens, and the view of it is highly interesting, blending as it does the beauty of nature with the ornaments of useful art, and the gaiety of animation of groups of well-dressed people."

THOMAS FLETCHER
(1787–1866), Philadelphia

78a.
Wine Cooler, about 1828–30

Silver, 12⅛ in. high
Marked (on the bottom): [pseudo-
hallmarks of a male bust, an eagle, the
letters "T" and "F" (for Thomas Fletcher)
and "P" (for Philadelphia)]
Engraved (on the side): EKH

EXHIBITED: Philadelphia Museum of Art,
1976, *Philadelphia: Three Centuries of American
Art,* no. 234 illus.

78b.
Design for Wine Cooler, about 1828–30

Pen and ink and wash on paper,
17¼ x 14 in.

The most important group of ornament
drawings for American silver of the Neo-
Classical period is the collection of
Fletcher designs in The Metropolitan
Museum of Art, New York. Based upon
the drawing shown here, this rare wine
cooler takes its inspiration from English
Regency sources. Marked with an array of
pseudo-hallmarks in the English manner,
it uses a vocabulary of ornament, however,
that is unmistakably Philadelphian and the
taste of Thomas Fletcher and the firm of
Fletcher & Gardiner. The work of this
firm represents the most important body
of silver produced in America during the
Neo-Classical period.

Wine Cooler: Private collection

Design for Wine Cooler: The Metropolitan
Museum of Art, New York, Whittelsey
Fund, 1953 (53.652.26)

ANTHONY G. QUERVELLE
(1789–1856), Philadelphia

79.
Center Table, about 1830

Mahogany, partially painted and gilded, with intarsia marble top, ormolu, and gilt brass, 29¹³⁄₁₆ x 34½ (diam.) in.
Labelled (twice, on either end of the crossbar support underneath the top): 126/ANTHONY G. QUERVELLE'S/ CABINET AND SOFA MANUFACTORY,/ SOUTH SECOND STREET, A FEW DOORS BELOW DOCK,/PHILADELPHIA

EXHIBITED: The Metropolitan Museum of Art, *19th Century America, Furniture and Other Decorative Arts* (1970), fig. 50

EX COLL.: [Joseph Sorger, Philadelphia, until 1968]

In America the center table became a fashionable new furniture form during the Neo-Classical period. Many of the finest examples were made in Philadelphia by Antoine-Gabriel Quervelle, who, like many other gifted French artisans of the early nineteenth century, among them the cabinetmaker Charles-Honoré Lannuier and the silversmith Simon Chaudron, had come to the United States as a fully trained artisan. By the time Quervelle labelled this table, about 1830, he had adopted "Anthony G. Quervelle" as the Anglicized version of his name.

This handsome center table, presumably inspired by a design published in George Smith's *Cabinet-Maker's and Uphol-sterer's Guide* of 1826, is closely related to three circular tables from Quervelle's workshop, commissioned in 1829 for the East Room of The White House, Washington, D.C. All of these tables incorporate the signature touches of Quervelle, such as heavily gadrooned borders, a marble inset center, gilt-brass moldings on the lower edge of the apron, and a tripartite base raised on robustly carved animal-paw feet. This example is further enhanced by the use of a specimen marble top, stenciled gilt patterns, and an ormolu collar at the juncture of the pedestal and base, which, along with the verde antique feet, has been enriched with touches of gilding.

The date of The White House commission and the fact that tables of this sort are fully described in *The Philadelphia Cabinet and Chair Maker's Union Book of Prices* for 1828 help to establish a date for this piece of about 1830.

The Metropolitan Museum of Art, New York, Edgar J. Kaufmann Charitable Foundation Fund (68.96)

80.
Cellarette, or *Wine Cooler*, Philadelphia, about 1820–25

Mahogany, with secondary woods of pine throughout except for tulip poplar inside the lions, gilded brass hardware, and zinc lining, 20¼ x 21⅜ x 27 in.

RECORDED: *cf.* Philadelphia Museum of Art, *Philadelphia, Three Centuries of American Art* (1976), pp. 265–266 no. 221 illus.

The design of this unusual cellarette, closely related to another in the Philadelphia Museum of Art, is derived from plates 94 and 98 in George Smith's *A Collection of Designs for Household Furniture and Interior Design*, published in London in 1808. It epitomizes the quality and sophistication of furniture produced in Philadelphia during the period of the Classical Revival.

THOMAS DOUGHTY
(1793–1856)

81.
Fishermen in a Landscape, about 1825–30

Oil on canvas, 12 x 17⅝ in.

Doughty's early landscapes depicted specific sites, such as the Fairmount Waterworks (see no. 76), but gradually his work developed a more poetic quality derived from the paintings of such Old Masters as Nicholas Poussin, Salvator Rosa, and Jacob Ruisdael, which he saw in the collection of his patron, Robert Gilmor, Jr., of Baltimore, and at exhibitions at the Pennsylvania Academy of the Fine Arts, Philadelphia.

This view, which may depict the area around the Delaware Water Gap, displays the atmospheric effects that characterize Doughty's work of the later 1820s. In a manner that was to become typical from this time forward, the artist has included several fishermen in his picture.

THOMAS SULLY
(1783–1872)

82.
Portrait of Samuel Henderson, 1833

Oil on canvas, 36 x 28 in.
Signed and dated (at lower right): 1833/TS

RECORDED: Charles Henry Hart, *A Register of Portraits Painted by Thomas Sully* (1908), p. 79 no. 738 // Edward Biddle and Mantle Fielding, *The Life and Works of Thomas Sully* (1921), p. 172 no. 766

Born in England, Samuel Henderson (1764–1841) emigrated to Montgomery, Pennsylvania, in 1782. There he founded the Henderson Marble Quarries which likely provided much of the marble for the Greek Revival buildings then being constructed in Philadelphia and other areas along the Schuylkill River. Henderson served as a Republican representative from Pennsylvania to the 13th United States Congress from 1814 to 1815, and then retired to his estate in Upper Merion.

As a wealthy citizen of Pennsylvania, Henderson naturally turned to Thomas Sully, Philadelphia's most prominent portrait artist, to execute his likeness. Here, Sully's bravura brushstroke and raking light add an element of drama typical of the Romantic portraiture of the day.

TUCKER FACTORIES
(active 1827–1838), Philadelphia

83a.
Pitcher with Floral Decoration, about
1827–38

Porcelain, painted and gilded, 9½ in. high

RECORDED: Alice Cooney Frelinghuysen,
American Porcelain 1770–1920 (1989), p. 18
fig. 12 this pitcher together with its
prototype (fig. 11) in "Tucker Pattern
Book I"

83b.
Pitcher with Landscape Decoration,
about 1827–38

Porcelain, painted and gilded,
8¹⁵⁄₁₆ in. high

The Tucker factories that operated in
Philadelphia from 1827 to 1838 produced
a variety of table and ornamental wares
inspired by French and English porcelains
of the early nineteenth century. Although
the design of the so-called "vase shape"
pitcher is distinctly Tucker, the quality of
decoration found on these pitchers varies
considerably depending on the skill of the
individual decorator and the anticipated
sale price of the piece. The floral pitcher
at the left, which closely follows a design
labelled "No. 58" in "Tucker Pattern Book
I" (Philadelphia Museum of Art), and the
landscape pitcher at the right are unusually
elaborate examples of their respective
types.

Mr. and Mrs. Stuart P. Feld

TUCKER FACTORIES
(active 1827–1838), Philadelphia

84.
Coffee, Tea and Dessert Service, about
1827–38

Porcelain, painted and gilded
Fruit baskets: 10⅛ x 9¼ in.
Coffee pot: 9¼ in. high
Tea pot: 5⅛ in. high

EXHIBITED: Philadelphia Museum of Art,
1957, *Tucker China, 1825–1838*, nos. 615–
630, lent by Mr. and Mrs. J. W. B.
Bausman, Jr.

EX COLL.: Mary Carpenter Smith Mayer
(Mrs. George Mayer), Lancaster, Penn-
sylvania, and by descent to Mr. and Mrs.
J. W. B. Bausman, III, Greenwich,
Connecticut

The survival of odd pieces of Tucker porcelain from different dinner and dessert services suggests that a variety of such services was produced at the various Tucker factories. Only a few that remain complete have been recorded, including a comprehensive dinner service with grisaille landscape decoration at "Wyck," Phila-delphia (see: Alice Cooney Frelinghuysen, *American Porcelain 1770–1920* [1989], pp. 86–87 pl. 8) and this coffee, tea, and dessert service which consists of two reticulated footed baskets, a coffee pot, two tea pots, a creamer, a covered sugar bowl, a waste bowl, two sweetmeat dishes, twelve cups and saucers, and twelve dessert plates. Each piece in the set bears the monogram "M C M" for Mary Carpenter Mayer (1784–1853), wife of Col. George Mayer, who was an ironmonger and hardware merchant of Lancaster, Pennsylvania. The pair of reticulated compotes with painted and gilded decoration appears to be unique, although their form follows a type familiar in both French and English services of this period. The design of the other pieces reflects English prototypes.

AMERICAN SCHOOL

85.
*View of the Fairmount Waterworks,
Philadelphia*, about 1835–38

Oil on canvas, 39¼ x 49½ in.

EX COLL.: sale 273, Samuel T. Freeman &
Co., Philadelphia, Sept. 1965; [David
David, Philadelphia, by 1969]; to [Hirschl
& Adler Galleries, New York, 1969]; to
private collection, 1969–91

Although it is not known who painted this
View of the Fairmount Waterworks, its date of
execution can be firmly established by the
structures depicted in it. First begun in
1812, the Fairmount Waterworks evolved
over a period of about forty years, with
buildings added as need or whim
warranted. In 1835, for example, the
gazebo shown on the dam at left was built
and the portico was added to the Federal-
style engine house at the very center of the
picture, thereby establishing the earliest
possible date for the painting. The covered
bridge depicted at the right burned down
in 1838, which suggests the latest date for
the picture. The figures in the right
foreground wear fashions typical of the
Jacksonian era.

ROBERT & WILLIAM WILSON
(active about 1825–1846), Philadelphia

86.
*Ewer with Presentation Inscription to
Mayor John Swift*, 1839

Silver, 15 in. high
Signed (on inside of foot): R & W
WILSON/STANDARD
Inscribed (on body, under spout): A token
of respect/TO/John Swift Esquire/LATE
MAYOR OF THE CITY OF PHILA./
PRESENTED/By/His Commissioned Offi-
cers/Jany. 15th . . 1839.

EX COLL.: Presented to Mayor John
Swift, Philadelphia, in 1839

The firm of R. & W. Wilson was among
the most highly respected silversmithing
establishments in Philadelphia in the
second quarter of the nineteenth century.
Stylistically, their work ranges from the
Classical Revival to the early Victorian
periods. Here, the bold use of classical
motifs, including the paw feet, bands of
egg and dart ornament, and repoussé
acanthus leaves parallels the flamboyant
Neo-Classicism of the Philadelphia
cabinetmaker Anthony Quervelle (see
no. 79) and his contemporaries.

John Swift, the recipient of this finely
wrought ewer, was admitted to the Bar in
Philadelphia in 1811. He served as Mayor
in the years 1832–38, 1839–41, and 1845–
49. This ewer was obviously presented to
him at the end of his first period in office.

Swift also received at least one other
silver presentation item, a large and elaborate five-piece tea and coffee service by
Edward Lownes (High Museum of Art,
Atlanta, Georgia), which was presented to
him in 1833 "by his Fellow Citizens as a
testimonial of their Gratitude for his
services at the Arch Street Prison . . .
during the prevalence of the Malignant
Cholera."

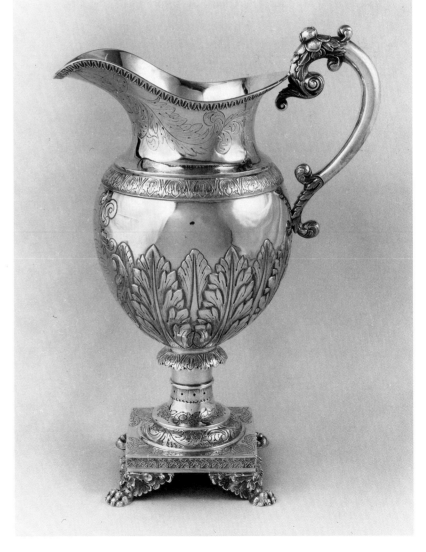

THOMAS BIRCH
(1779–1851)

87.
View of Philadelphia Harbor, about
1835–40

Oil on canvas, 20 x 30¼ in.
Signed and inscribed (on the back, before
lining): Philadelphia/Painted by/Th.
[illeg.] Birch/Phila.

EX COLL.: Sandor collection; to sale 1240,
Parke-Bernet Galleries, New York, Apr. 7,
1951, no. 271 illus.; to private collection,
1951–89

Thomas Birch began his career as an
apprentice and assistant to his father,
William Birch, by contributing drawings
for plates in their *Views of Philadelphia*,
published in 1800. Although the younger
Birch gained renown for painting
portraits, naval engagements, and marine
compositions, he continued to document
Philadelphia landmarks, especially those
adjacent to the city's waterfront. Here, the
view looks up the Delaware River from
below the United States Navy Yard. To
the left of the Navy Yard is Sparks' Shot
Tower, a munitions factory that operated
between 1808 and 1907. The skyline of
the city of Philadelphia, shown in the
background, is punctuated by the
imposing tower and spire of Christ
Church, completed in 1754.

Attributed to THOMAS S. RENSHAW and JOHN BARNHART (active about 1814–1829), Baltimore

88.
Armchair, about 1815

Cherry wood, painted and gilded, with caning, 33⅛ in. high

By the beginning of the nineteenth century, Baltimore had become the leading center for paint-decorated furniture in America. More than forty makers of painted furniture were listed in the city directories during the period 1800–40.

This painted and gilded armchair, ornamented with chinoiserie scenes, is probably the collaboration of the cabinet-maker Thomas S. Renshaw and the ornamental painter John Barnhart. The attribution is based on its relationship to a settee signed by Renshaw and Barnhart (Baltimore Museum of Art; see: William Voss Elder, III, *Baltimore Painted Furniture 1800–1840* [Baltimore Museum of Art, 1972], pp. 42–43 no. 20 illus.). The unusually shaped crest rail and the style and quality of the decoration are also closely related to another side chair attributed to Renshaw and Barnhart (Elder, p. 44 fig. 21).

Like much of the earlier painted furniture made in Baltimore, the design of these pieces was probably adapted from various plates in books published in London by Thomas Sheraton.

The Henry Francis du Pont Winterthur Museum

89.

Painted Klismos-Form Side Chair,
Baltimore, about 1820–30

Maple, painted, with stenciled and
freehand gilt decoration, 34 in. high

RECORDED: The Metropolitan Museum
of Art, New York, *19th Century America,
Furniture and Other Decorative Arts* (1970),
no. 46 (one of the set) // William Voss
Elder, III, *Baltimore Painted Furniture 1800–
1840* (Baltimore Museum of Art, 1972),
p. 61 no. 36 (one of the set)

EX COLL.: Abell family, Baltimore

This chair, one of a set made for
"Woodbourne," the home of the Abell
family of Baltimore, is among the most
successful adaptations of the Roman
version of the Greek klismos-form chair
made in America. Probably inspired by
designs published in London in 1807 by
Thomas Hope, they are distinguished by
the graceful sweep of the back, the broad
curvilinear crest rail, and the turned front
legs with inset cuffs. The decoration of
the crestrail, which is slightly different on
each chair, incorporates griffins, unicorns,
and other mythological animals; it was
most likely derived from plate 56 of
Thomas Sheraton's *The Cabinet Maker and
Upholsterer's Drawing-Book,* published in
London in 1802. Similar decoration can be
found on an extensive suite of painted
furniture made for Alexander Brown of
Baltimore (Elder, figs. 49–53). Both sets
relate to the architect Benjamin Henry
Latrobe's designs for a set of furniture
ordered by President James H. Madison
for the Oval Room of The White House
in 1809 from the shop of John and Hugh
Finlay of Baltimore, which may provide a
clue to the authorship of these chairs.

The Metropolitan Museum of Art, Gift
of Mrs. Paul Moore, 1965 (65.167.6)

CHARLES BIRD KING
(1785–1862)

90.
Portrait of Mrs. Joseph Gales, Jr., about 1821

Oil on canvas, 52 x 40 in.

RECORDED: Andrew F. Cosentino, *The Paintings of Charles Bird King (1785–1862)* (1977), pp. 134 no. 86 illus. // The Junior League of the City of Washington, D.C., *The City of Washington: An Illustrated History* (1977), p. 95 illus.

EXHIBITED: The Textile Museum, Washington, D.C., 1954, *Primarily American: An Exhibit of 17th, 18th and 19th Century Heirlooms*, p. 1

EX COLL.: Mrs. Joseph Gales, Jr., Washington, D.C.; by descent to Mrs. Charles W. Exton, Washington, D.C., by 1954

Mrs. Sarah Juliana Maria Lee Gales (about 1798–1879) was a member of the illustrious Lee family of Virginia. As the wife of Joseph Gales, Jr. (1786–1860), Mayor of Washington, D.C., from 1827 to 1830, she was among the most prominent hostesses in Washington society.

This portrait was executed by Charles Bird King while he was in Washington painting his celebrated series of Indian portraits. Mrs. Gales is portrayed in the elegant style of the period, with her Empire dress and hairstyle in the latest French fashion, beside a Neo-Classical piano with brass and ormolu decoration. In 1821 King designed the Gales' home, "Eckington," in Greek Revival style. This portrait was probably painted at that time.

WILLIAM MacLEOD
(1811–1892)

91.
View of the City of Washington from the Anacostia Shore, 1856

Oil on canvas, 38 x 54 in.
Signed and dated (at lower right): Wm MacLeod.1856

RECORDED: Andrew J. Cosentino and Henry H. Glassie, *The Capital Image: Painters in Washington, 1800–1915* (1983), p. 105

EXHIBITED: Baltimore Museum of Art, 1988, *Maryland Collects: American Paintings from 1750 to 1900* (no cat.)

EX COLL.: Brune Family Estate, Baltimore, until 1984; to private collection, Baltimore, 1984–91

In every aspect of its design, the City of Washington, D.C. was the culmination of early efforts to establish a national identity based on Greek precedents. Laid out according to the plan of the Frenchman Pierre Charles L'Enfant (1755–1825), Washington became the quintessential classical city in the United States, not only in its plan, but also in the buildings and monuments that soon began to ornament it. Visible in the distance of this view by Alexandria-born painter William Mac-

Leod are, from left to right, the half-completed Washington Monument, the Department of the Treasury, the romantically picturesque "Castle" of the Smithsonian Institution, the original flat classical dome of the Capitol (to be replaced by the present dome in 1863), and the Navy Yard. The figure sketching in the foreground may be a self-portrait of the artist, who was later to serve as the first Curator of the Corcoran Gallery of Art in Washington.

MADE FOR THE AMERICAN MARKET – IMPORTS FROM ABROAD

JEAN-BAPTISTE DUBUC
(active 1790–1819), Paris

92.
Clock with Figure of George Washington,
about 1815

Ormolu, with enamel dial, and clock
works, 19⅛ in. high
Marked (on the dial): Dubuc/Rue
Michell-le-Comte No. 33/A Paris.
Inscribed (below the eagle): E PLURIBUS
UNUM; (below the dial): WASHINGTON.
/First in WAR, First in PEACE/First in the
HEARTS of his COUNTRYMEN.

Made in Paris for the American market,
this clock is one of several variants
featuring different full-length figures and
busts of our first President. Although
examples bearing the names of Arsandaux
and Henry Voisin have been recorded,
most seem to be by Dubuc.

The sources for the various figures
and busts of Washington have not been
fully studied, but the full-length figure of
Washington that ornaments this clock
seems to have been taken from one of
John Trumbull's full-length portraits of
Washington, presumably known through
an engraving. Of the relief at the center of
the base, Donald L. Fennimore, Curator in
Charge of Metals at Winterthur, writes in

the manuscript of a forthcoming catalogue
of the copper and brass collections at
Winterthur: "The plaque ... shows
Washington receiving a sword from the
Head of State, symbolic of the authority
given him as Commander-in-Chief of
Revolutionary forces. In doing so, he was
likened to the great Roman citizen-soldier
Cincinnatus, around whom the Society of
the Cincinnati ... was founded."

The Henry Francis du Pont Winterthur
Museum

THOMAS MESSENGER & SONS,
Birmingham, England

Retailed by J. & I. COX, New York

93.
Set of Three Argand Lamps, about
1825–30

Bronze, with matte and burnished gilt
patination, and frosted and cut glass
shades, glass prisms, and chimneys
Two smaller lamps: 21 in. high (overall)
Larger center lamp: 23 in. high (overall)
Marked (on embossed brass labels attached
to each): J & I. Cox/New York
Marked (on topside of iron plate inside
base of each): MESSENGER'S [illeg.]; (on
underside of base, above iron plate of
each): MESSENGER'S

For many years the presence of brass labels
embossed with American names on
Classical Revival lamps led to the conclusion that these lamps were made in the
United States. Although this suite of
lamps is marked "J & I. Cox/New York,"
the hidden side of a cast iron plate inside
the base bears the name of Messenger's,
which appears to have been the most
important firm manufacturing decorative
metalwork in Birmingham, England, at
this time. Possibly some American
retailers were able to offer exclusive
designs, as there appears to be some
correlation between specific designs and
the firms that marketed them. The New

York directories list the firms of J. & J.
and J. & I. Cox variously as "lamp and
hardware" and "lamp and oil store" at
different Maiden Lane locations from
1819 to 1830.

This set of lamps is particularly
distinguished by its imposing scale and
the survival of its original matte and
burnished gilt finish in pristine condition.

94.
"Old Paris" Porcelain Covered Soup Tureen and Undertray, French, about 1830

Retailed by Baldwin Gardiner, New York, 1833

Porcelain, painted and gilded
Tureen: 12 x 15⅛ in.
Undertray: 15 1/16 in. long

RECORDED: Douglas R. Kent, "Hyde Hall, Otsego County, New York," in *The Magazine Antiques*, XCII (Aug. 1967), p. 190

EX COLL.: [Baldwin Gardiner, New York, 1833]; to George Clarke (1768–1835), "Hyde Hall," Cooperstown, New York, 1833–35, and by descent in the family, until 1984

Our knowledge of the specific character of glass and porcelain imported by American retailers during the Neo-Classical period is limited because so little of that material is identifiable today. This soup tureen and undertray are from an extensive dinner service purchased by George Clarke for his splendid Classical Revival residence, "Hyde Hall," at Cooperstown, New York. A statement dated November 1833 documents Clarke's considerable purchases from retailer Baldwin Gardiner's "FUR-NISHING WAREHOUSE" at 149 Broadway, New York, including the acquisition on April 18 of "One porcelain Dinning [*sic*] and dessr [*sic*] Service, rich bouquet and yellow border" for the sum of $500.00, which appears to have been the most expensive item among Clarke's many purchases from Gardiner.

Private collection

95.

Pair of "Old Paris" Porcelain Vases with Portraits of John Adams and Thomas Jefferson, French, about 1825–30

Porcelain, painted and gilded,
13⅛ in. high

EX COLL.: Mr. and Mrs. Guillaume Merl, Brooklyn, New York, and by descent, until 1976

Although the few attempts in the early nineteenth century to establish porcelain manufactories in the United States — Tucker in Philadelphia and Decasse & Chenou in New York, among them — were commercially unsuccessful, quantities of porcelain were imported into the United States from England and France. Some of this porcelain was made specifically for the American market, including this splendid pair of vases that are decorated with portraits of Presidents John Adams and Thomas Jefferson, as well as a bust of Benjamin Franklin, all of whom had served as American diplomats in France. The portraits are based on two lithographs from a suite of five drawn on stone by the eminent French lithographer Nicholas Maurin, after portraits by Gilbert Stuart, and printed in Boston by John B. Pendleton for John Doggett. The coupling of Adams and Jefferson may have resulted from the fact that they both died on the same day, July 4, 1826, the fiftieth anniversary of America's Independence, a coincidence unlikely to have escaped the notice of European entrepreneurs eager to please a burgeoning American market.

Mr. and Mrs. Stuart P. Feld

96.
"Old Paris" Porcelain Crater-Form Vase with Two Views in Philadelphia, French, about 1830

Porcelain, painted and gilded,
15 9/16 x 11 1/4 in. (at top)
RECORDED: Hirschl & Adler Galleries, New York, *The State of the Arts* (1990), p. 76 fig. 7.2

EX COLL.: [dealer, Baltimore area, 1972]; to The Dietrich American Foundation, Philadelphia, 1972–88; to private collection

Like the pair of Paris porcelain vases saluting three American diplomats to France (see no. 95), this vase, depicting a *View on the Schuylkill River, from the Old Waterworks* on one side and *The Bank of Pennsylvania* on the other, was made for the American market and presumably was originally the mate to a vase now in the Philadelphia Museum of Art, which shows views of *The Second Bank of the United States* and *The Dam and Fairmount Waterworks.* The building partially visible in the right foreground of the view along the Schuylkill is the Old Waterworks, which, at the very moment this vase was being made in Paris, housed the only ceramic manufactory in America capable of competing with French work of this quality. A Tucker factory occupied this site from 1827 to 1832, producing the finest American porcelain of the early nineteenth century.

Mr. and Mrs. Stuart P. Feld

After JOHN JAMES AUDUBON
(1785–1851)

Engraved by ROBERT HAVELL
(1793–1878)

97a.
Mocking Bird, plate XXI from *The Birds of America*, London, 1827–38

Hand-colored aquatint with etching and engraving, 33 x 23¼ in.

97b.
Common American Swan, plate CCCCXI from *The Birds of America*, London, 1827–38

Hand-colored aquatint with etching and engraving, 25⅛ x 38 in.

Common American Swan.
CYGNUS AMERICANUS, Sharpless
Nymphæa Flava - Leitner

The scientific revolution that spawned the great colorplate ornithologies, of which Audubon's was preeminent, was characterized by an empirical approach modelled upon ancient precedent. What set Audubon apart from his peers, however, was his introduction of drama to scientific illustration, an innovation which exactly paralleled the development of Romantic landscape painting from the tradition of the topographical view.

Audubon's *Mocking Bird* is not merely an ornitholigically correct illustration, but in fact achieves its first effect upon the viewer as a powerful allegory of the terror attending the struggle between life and death. As the first of Audubon's prints reached his subscribers, similar themes were being explored by the artists of the emerging Hudson River School of landscape painting, and particularly by Thomas Cole.

It is somewhat ironic that Audubon's publication, celebrated among nineteenth-century Americana, is, in fact, the product of a British press. The artist's initial efforts to gain the support of the American scientific community met with resistance from the followers of Alexander Wilson, the author of the first comprehensive study of the topic published in this country, *American Ornithology.*

Undeterred, Audubon embarked on a tour of Scotland and England where, through the encouragement of the scientific societies of Glasgow, Edinburgh, and London, his attempts to enlist subscribers met with immediate success. While in London Audubon solicited the collaboration of the engraver Robert Havell, Jr., arguably the most talented aquatint engraver of his day. Publication of the sumptuous portfolio was a massive undertaking without precedent and required eleven years to complete.

129

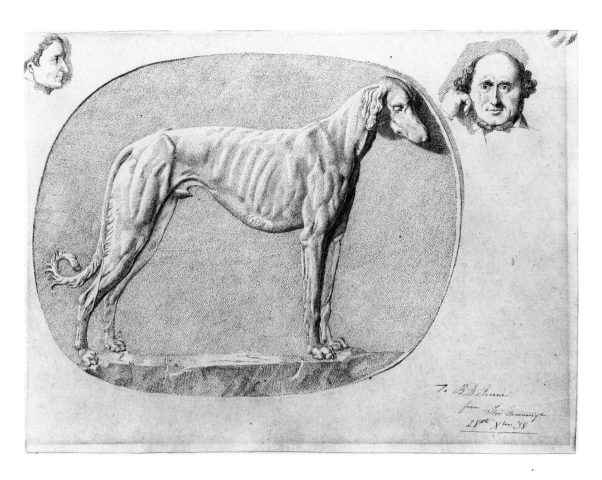

To BD Greene
from Hor Greenough
28th Xber '38

HORATIO GREENOUGH
(1805–1852)

98.
*Study of a Greyhound, with Portraits of
Hiram Powers and Luigi Persico*, 1838

Sepia ink on paper, 8¾ x 12⁵⁄₁₆ in.
Signed, dated, and inscribed (at lower
right): To BD Greene/from/Hor
Greenough/28th Xber '38; (on the back):
Persico. // Powers.

RECORDED: Nathalia Wright, *Horatio
Greenough: The First American Sculptor* (1963),
pp. 201, 343 fn. 21 // Letter, Nathalia
Wright, to the owner of the drawing, Feb.
10, 1982 (Hirschl & Adler archives)

EX COLL.: Benjamin Daniel Greene
(1793–1863), Boston, in 1838

Originally from Boston, Horatio Greenough was the first American sculptor to
live and work in Italy. He went initially to
Rome in 1825 with an introduction to the
great Danish Neo-Classical sculptor,
Bertel Thorwaldsen; in 1828 he established
himself in Florence, where he remained
for most of the rest of his life. Greenough's path to Italy became the norm for
American sculptors, and for the next half
century he was followed there by a
succession of artists seeking to work in
marble in the Neo-Classical style.

This drawing was a gift from the
sculptor to Benjamin D. Greene of
Boston, who, along with his wife, visited
the Greenoughs in Florence during the
winter of 1838–39. Mrs. Greene and
Louisa G. Greenough had been childhood
friends in Boston. According to Nathalia
Wright (1982), the drawing appears to be

a study for a bas relief, a form in which
Greenough became interested in his later
years, and undoubtedly depicts his greyhound, Arno. Greenough also created a
marble sculpture, in the round, of Arno
about the same time (Museum of Fine
Arts, Boston).

The small portraits in the drawing
are likenesses of the sculptors Hiram
Powers (1805–1873), one of Greenough's
fellow Americans living and working in
Florence (see no. 100), and the Neapolitan
Luigi Persico (1791–1860), who, along
with Greenough, created sculptures for the
United States Capitol, Washington, D.C.

Private collection

After THOMAS CRAWFORD
(1813–1857)

99.
Studio Record of Thomas Crawford, about
1842–55: *"The Genius of Mirth,"* after a
model of 1842

Leather-bound book, 22½ x 17 x 1½ in.
This drawing: pencil on paper,
17½ x 13⁷⁄₁₆ in.
Book inscribed (on the front): CRAW-
FORD; (at lower right, in crest): I BIDE MY
TIME; (below crest): MARION CRAWFORD

EX COLL.: by descent in the Crawford
family to Countess Eleonora Marion-
Crawford Rocca, Sorrento, Italy, granddaughter of the sculptor; to private
collection, until 1980

This drawing is part of a leather-bound
portfolio containing renderings of more
than thirty-five sculptures by Thomas
Crawford. Since several of the drawings,
which are all stylistically related, bear the
signature of either Leonardo Camia or
P. Guglielmi, it seems likely that all were
executed by one of these two men, based
on the original plaster models or finished
marbles in Crawford's studio. (Camia is
documented as having worked in the
sculptor's studio, and Guglielmi
undoubtedly was an assistant as well.)
Taken as a whole, the flawlessly executed
drawings serve as an important record of
the work of one of America's most
significant Neo-Classical sculptors.

Crawford was among the earliest
American sculptors to migrate to Italy,
where he began receiving commissions for
portrait busts of wealthy Americans
making the Grand Tour. He also created
idealized works of classical subject matter,
as well as "fancy pieces" depicting children
usually engaged in musical pursuits, as in
the sculpture represented here, *The Genius
of Mirth*, which was modeled in 1842 and
carved into marble the following year
(The Metropolitan Museum of Art, New
York).

Among the other sculptures depicted
in the portfolio are *Bust of Louisa Ward
Crawford Terry (Mrs. Thomas Crawford)*,
1847 (Museum of the City of New York);
Flora, 1853 (The Newark Museum, New
Jersey); *Boy Playing Marbles*, 1853 (Worcester
Art Museum, Massachusetts); *Christian
Pilgrim in Sight of Rome*, 1847, and *Adam and
Eve After Their Expulsion*, 1855 (both,
Boston Athenaeum); and ten drawings for
The Progress of Civilization, Crawford's
design for the East Pediment of the Senate
Wing, U.S. Capitol, Washington, D.C.,
completed posthumously in 1863.

Library of Hirschl & Adler Galleries

HIRAM POWERS
(1805–1873)

100.
Proserpine (or *Persephone*), modeled in
1838–39

Marble, with gilding in incised
inscription, 15½ in. high
Signed and inscribed (on the socle, at
back): HIRAM POWERS/SCULP.
Inscribed (on the socle, at front):
Proserpine

Along with Horatio Greenough (see
no. 98) and Thomas Crawford (see
no. 99), Hiram Powers was one of the
triumvirate of American sculptors first to
travel to Italy to live and work. There,
these sculptors and their followers found
at work the great European masters of the
Neo-Classical school of sculpture, An-
tonio Canova and Bertel Thorwaldsen, as
well as an ample supply of skilled stone-
cutters to translate their plaster models
into marble.

Powers gained considerable recognition in Italy, producing marble portrait
busts, allegorical and classicizing figures,
and idealized busts. *Proserpine* of 1838–39
was one of his earliest idealized busts and
would become his most frequently
commissioned work. The first version was
life-size and featured a decorative acanthus
leaf molding around its lower edge.
Among the later variants is this
"abbreviated" half-scale bust, which
appears to be considerably rarer than the
full-size examples of the subject. Its
simplicity and delicate size make it one of
the most appealing of all the sculptures
produced during the Classical Revival.

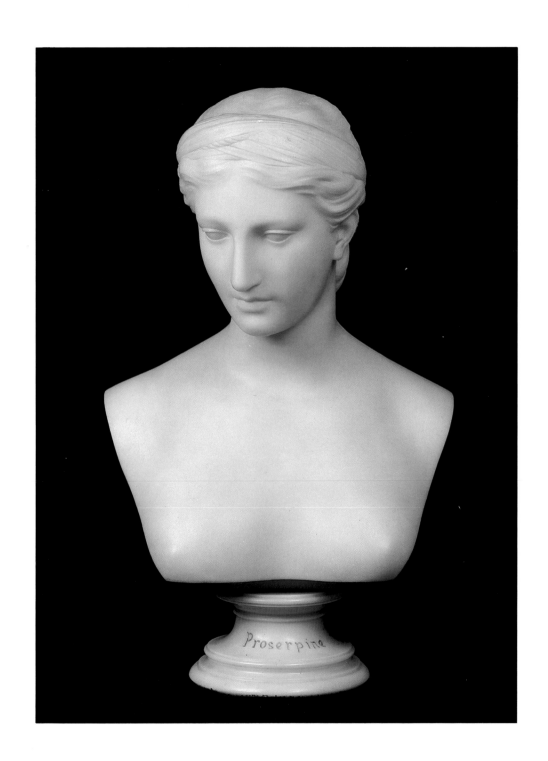

Index

Designed by Harakawa Sisco Inc

Typeset in Centaur and Arrighi
by The Sarabande Press

Printed on Cameo dull 100 lb. text and
Cameo dull 100 lb. cover
by Colorcraft Lithographers, Inc.